Frontispiece: Les Demoiselles d'Avignon 1906–7, 96 × 92in. *The Museum of Modern Art, New York* (34)

The Arts Council of Great Britain 1960

Picasso

At The Tate Gallery · 6 July to 18 September

Admission 3/6, Students 1/9

Weekdays 10–8, Sundays 2–8

Second edition

Printed in Great Britain by Lund Humphries, London and Bradford

Foreword

Ever since the last war the Arts Council has been contemplating the arrangement of a major retrospective Picasso exhibition. The initiation of the project owes much to the enthusiasm of my predecessor Philip James, who was responsible for the organization of four previous exhibitions devoted to Picasso's work: lithographs in 1948, paintings, sculpture, graphic work and ceramics in 1950, an exhibition of ceramics in 1957 and a large exhibition of graphic art in 1956. Many other countries, however, have held retrospective exhibitions, and it was difficult to select a date that would not clash with these and would not necessitate calling on owners to lend too soon again. Our plans had, therefore, to be deferred more than once, but it is now London's opportunity to see a large and representative exhibition of the work of the outstanding artist of our time.

Picasso's output is immense, and it would be impossible adequately to represent his range in all the mediums in which he has worked in one exhibition of manageable size. This exhibition is, therefore, confined to his paintings.

The Council is deeply grateful to the artist for the interest he has taken in the exhibition from the beginning, and for his indispensable personal help and advice. Monsieur Picasso has been particularly generous in lending a hundred pictures from his own collection, which he has taken great trouble to select. We wish to add to our thanks to him our recognition of the invaluable help given by Madame Jacqueline Roque, for whose assistance throughout we are most grateful.

The Arts Council has been particularly fortunate in persuading Mr Roland Penrose to make the choice of pictures and to write the catalogue. Mr Penrose's long-standing friendship with the artist and exceptional knowledge of his work have made him singularly well qualified to undertake these tasks. We are extremely grateful to him for his unsparing efforts during the last two years to assemble as fine an exhibition as possible.

Special thanks are due to all the owners who have participated in this exhibition. It was with some diffidence that the Council asked them to deprive themselves once again of their paintings. Their generosity can be measured by the list of lenders given elsewhere in this catalogue, from which few important collectors of Picasso's work are missing.

We are particularly indebted to the following for their help: Mr Alfred H. Barr, Jr., and Mr William S. Lieberman, of the

Museum of Modern Art, New York, who never failed to give information and advice when called upon and who were responsible for securing the loan of many pictures; Monsieur Daniel-Henry Kahnweiler, Madame Leiris and Monsieur Maurice Jardot for their wise counsel on many occasions; Monsieur Jaimé Sabartès, Monsieur Jean Cassou, Director of the Musée Nationale d'Art Moderne, and Monsieur Bernard Dorival, Conservateur, for valuable information; Mr and Mrs Victor W. Ganz, Monsieur Siegfried Rosengart and Monsieur Heinz Berggruen for generous help and advice; Madame Cuttoli, Monsieur Fin Vilato, Monsieur and Madame Xavier Vilato and the Princesse Guy de Broglie for help in securing loans; Mr Stefan Munsing of the United States Information Services, Mr William N. Eisendrath, Curator of Paintings at the City Art Museum, St Louis and Señor Xavier de Salas, Director of the Spanish Institute in London, for valuable assistance.

Many other have generously given their assistance and among these we wish specially to thank the following:

Monsieur Pierre Baudouin, Monsieur and Madame Bernier, Dr H. Carey Walker, Mr Henry Clifford, Mr David D. Duncan, Dr Bernhard Geiser, Messrs Charles and Peter Gimpel, Monsieur Robert Giron, Dr Otto Hammacher, Sir Philip Hendy, Monsieur Claude Hersain, Mr Gustav Kahnweiler, Monsieur Emile Langui, Monsieur and Madame Peter Lyon, Mr Frederic H. Major, Mr John Maxon, Mr and Mrs Tony Mayer, Monsieur and Madame Franz Meyer, Mr D. J. Muir, La Vicomtesse de Noailles, Mrs Margaret Plass, Mrs Lee Miller Penrose, Monsieur and Madame Ramier, Sir Herbert Read, Miss Joyce Reeves, Mr Andrew Ritchie, Mrs John D. Rockefeller III, Mr and Mrs John Russell, Mr and Mrs Daniel Saidenberg, Dr Georg Schmidt, Mr James Thrall Soby, Mr Justin K. Thannhauser, Dr Wehrli, Mr John Witt, Monsieur Christian Zervos.

The Trustees of the Tate Gallery readily made available as many galleries as were required, and this at great inconvenience to themselves and to their staff. We would like to thank them, the Director, Sir John Rothenstein, Mr Norman Reid, the Keeper and Mr Ronald Alley, Deputy Keeper, most warmly for their sympathetic co-operation, without which it is not possible to hold these large exhibitions in London.

GABRIEL WHITE *Director of Art*

Introduction   by Roland Penrose

The name which predominates in the development of the arts during this century, and to which the most revolutionary changes are inevitably ascribed, is that of Pablo Picasso. It is, moreover, largely due to him that the conception of art as a powerful emotional medium, rather than a search for the perfection of ideal forms of beauty, has become accepted among the artists of our time. The return to a fundamental belief that art should spring from a primitive need to express our feelings towards the world around us in strong emotional terms makes us more prone to value a work of art for its vitality than for its perfection. It is the exceptional power of Picasso's work that compels us, in return, to discover in it the mysterious presence of beauty.

Early in life doubt, and dissatisfaction with academic formulas, brought him to discover that a search for beauty according to the standards in which he had been brought up was not the aim he wished to pursue. The brilliance of his talent as a youth and the ease with which he absorbed the work of other great contemporary artists could have tempted him to become satisfied with the success that came to him at last after years of poverty in Barcelona and Paris, but the strength of his powers of expression coupled with an unusual degree of courage brought a crisis which forced him to abandon the easy road to fame and plunge perilously into new forms of creation.

The turning-point in Picasso's early career came when he was 25. The struggle in which the young artist found himself involved is forcibly illustrated in the great picture, *Les Demoiselles d'Avignon* (cat. no.34), painted in Paris in the spring of 1907. It came as a shock to his friends that he should abandon a style that they had grown to love and produce instead a form of art that they could no longer understand. No one, not even Matisse, Braque and Derain, nor his devoted patrons, nor even his close friend and admirer Guillaume Apollinaire could stomach this work, which at first sight seemed to them outrageous. It took many months to digest this insult to their sensibility, but gradually they came not only to accept it but to find that it was exerting a profound influence on them. Apollinaire, when he realized the significance of the change that had taken place in the artist as well as in his work, wrote a description of the difference between two kinds of artists: those who follow their impulses and show no signs of struggle, who 'are like a prolongation of nature' and whose works 'pass in no way through the intellect', and other artists who, in solitude, 'must draw everything from within themselves'. 'Picasso', he states, 'was an artist of the former kind. Never has there been so fantastic a spectacle as the metamorphosis he went through in becoming an artist of the second kind.'*

This courage to explore the unknown, which has never forsaken Picasso, led in the years that followed to the creation of a new style, cubism. Working in close collaboration with his friend Georges Braque, he was responsible for one of the major revolutions in the art of our time, a revolution which revised the relationship of painting to reality and widened the scope of our vision and our understanding of the world. Although since that time the work of Picasso has not always been cubist in style, the discoveries made between 1909 and the outbreak of the 1914 war (which ended his close association with Braque), have led to innumerable developments in his work and have spread their influence more widely than any other single movement in the arts. One of the main characteristics of his work is the ease with which he can vary his style and often mingle styles which might seem incompatible in the same painting. This tendency has in fact increased as time has passed and his experience in the various forms of expression which he employs has grown richer. In his career it is remarkable how little of his former discoveries is lost. A visual memory of prodigious accuracy enables him to hold years of experience at his disposal, and contributes to the speed and urgency with which he is able to work. This retentiveness does not apply only to technical discoveries. He has been preoccupied throughout his life by images and events that possess a peculiar significance for him. The enveloping tenderness of maternity, the wonder of the human head, the dilemma of the artist in relation to his model, the sacrificial drama of the bullfight, the heroism of classical myths, the metamorphosis of living beings and inanimate objects, the mystery of landscape or the familiar domesticity of a still life: these themes have always absorbed him.

Although Picasso has lived by far the greater part of his life in France he has never forgotten his Spanish origins. Born in Malaga in 1881, he was the son of José Ruiz Blasco and Maria Picasso Lopez. He received his first instruction in the arts from his father who was a mediocre painter but who had the virtue of encouraging his son and who realized that the boy's talent, at the age of 13, already greatly surpassed his own. After early training in the academic

* Guillaume Apollinaire, *Cubist Painters* (English trans.), New York, 1944.

tradition at art schools in Corunna, Barcelona and Madrid, where he passed his entrance examinations brilliantly, he rapidly outgrew the instruction that these academies were able to offer. Barcelona, where his family had settled, proved to be too provincial an atmosphere for him and he sought the more brilliant international stimulus of Paris. Even so, the habits, the temperament, and the art of Picasso are still fundamentally Spanish, and the early influences absorbed by him are not limited to the discoveries he made in Paris but spring also from the art of his native land.

Picasso's faithfulness to the country from which he has exiled himself is an example of the many paradoxes which are characteristic of his life and his work. For instance, he can convey with extraordinary tenderness the intimacy of lovers and yet submit the female form to a scathing visual analysis. There seems to be no limit to the distortions he can invent for the human body and yet no artist has more compassion for human anguish. He is a revolutionary who understands and loves tradition, and a creator so essentially concerned with life that he is often obsessed by the grim reality of death. Novelty and invention fascinate him as they do a child, but there is also a continuity which runs throughout his work, giving it the constant imprint of his genius. His capacity to invent new styles and techniques, a gift that has often bewildered both his admirers and his critics, is not a fickle disregard for his former loves, it is rather a means of saving himself from the sterility of repetition, and keeping us perpetually astonished at the youthfulness and penetration of his vision.

The output which has come from Picasso's untiring energy is prodigious. It is inconceivable owing to its sheer volume that the majority of his most important works in painting alone could be combined in one exhibition. Although painting is his major art, the universality of his genius extends to sculpture, drawing, etching and ceramics, murals and designs for the theatre, poetry, the writing of plays, and the cinema. His enormous influence on the art of our time is due to the vigour and the lack of prejudice with which he develops these diverse means of expression. No artist can afford to ignore him and those who have found inspiration in his work are countless. No contemporary style, from surrealism or expressionism in their various forms to the most unemotional geometric abstraction, escapes his influence and in innumerable cases he is the prophet and the forerunner of new trends.

The work of Picasso is more than a mirror of our times; it opens our eyes to the future. Its vitality and its insight, its tenderness and its violence, are born of an understanding and a love for humanity. His art goes far beyond a facile enchantment of the eye. It fulfils a more essential purpose – the intensification of feeling and the education of the spirit. Picasso looks at the world with new vision, and by his art he enables us to do likewise.

Short Bibliography

Books dealing with the life and work of Picasso are now too numerous all to be listed here. A comprehensive bibliography, up to 1946, is given in Alfred H. Barr's *Picasso: Fifty Years of his Art*. Those mentioned below are the most important works of reference, or the most recently published. The abbreviations used in referring to these books in the catalogue notes appear to the left.

G. Apollinaire, *Les Peintres Cubistes*, Paris, 1913 (English tr., *The Cubist Painters*, New York, 1944)

Barr   A. H. Barr, Jr, *Picasso: Fifty Years of his Art*, New York, 1946

W. Boeck and J. Sabartès, *Pablo Picasso*, London, 1955

L.-G. Buchheim, *Picasso*, London, 1959

C.A.   *Cahiers d'Art*, Paris, 1926 – see especially: 7 no.3/5, 1932; 10, no.7/10, 1935; 12, no.4/5, 1937; 13, no.3/10, 1938; 23, no.1, 1948; 25, no.2, 1950

A. Cirici-Pellicer, *Picasso Antes de Picasso*, Barcelona, 1946 (French tr. *Picasso avant Picasso*, Geneva, 1950)

D. D. Duncan, *The Private World of Pablo Picasso*, New York, 1957

F. Elgar and R. Maillard, *Picasso*, Paris/London, 1955

P. Eluard, *A Pablo Picasso*, Geneva/Paris, 1947

Geiser   B. Geiser, *Pablo Picasso: Fifty-five Years of his Graphic Work*, London, 1955. *Picasso: Peintre-graveur, Catalogue illustré de l'œuvre gravé et lithographié, 1899–1931*, Berne, 1955

J. Golding, *Cubism: A History and Analysis, 1907–1914*, London, 1959

H. and S. Janis, *Picasso: The Recent Years, 1939–46*, New York, 1946

D.-H. Kahnweiler, *The Rise of Cubism*, New York, 1949

J. Larrea, *Guernica*, New York, 1947

A. Level, *Picasso*, Paris, 1928

W. S. Lieberman, *Picasso: Blue and Rose Periods*, New York, 1952

H. F. Mackenzie, *Understanding Picasso*, Chicago, 1940

R. Melville, *Picasso: Master of the Phantom*, London, 1939

F. Mourlot, *Picasso Lithographe*, 3 vols, Monte Carlo, 1949–56

F. Olivier, *Picasso et ses Amis*, Paris, 1933,

H. Parmelin, *Picasso sur la Place*, Paris, 1959

R. Penrose, *Homage to Picasso*, London, 1951. *Portrait of Picasso*, London, 1956. *Picasso: His Life and Work*, London, 1958

M. Raynal, *Pablo Picasso*, Paris, 1922. *Picasso*, Geneva, 1953

J. Richardson, *Picasso, Aquarelle und gouachen*, Basel, 1956

C. Roy, *La Guerre et la Paix*, Paris, 1954

J. Sabartès, *Picasso: Portraits et Souvenirs*, Paris, 1946. *Picasso: Documents Iconographiques*, Geneva, 1954. *Picasso, Les Menines et la Vie*, Paris, 1958

G. Stein, *Picasso*, Paris/New York/London, 1938

A. Vallentin, *Picasso*, Paris, 1957

Z   C. Zervos, *Pablo Picasso, 1895–1940* (in progress), vols. 1–10, Paris, 1932–1959

Exhibition Catalogues

This short list is restricted to catalogues of exhibitions of special interest, or to those containing useful introductions or notes.

London: The Leicester Galleries, *Picasso and Matisse*, 1919
Munich: Galerie Thannhauser, *Picasso*, 1922
Paris: Galerie Georges Petit, *Picasso*, 1932
Zurich: Kunsthaus, *Picasso*, 1932
London: New Burlington Galleries, *Guernica*, 1938
London: London Bulletin, no.15/16, 15 May 1939, Catalogue of an exhibition *Picasso in English Collections*, held at the London Gallery, 1939
New York: Museum of Modern Art, *Picasso, Forty Years of his Art*, 1939
London: L'Association Française d'Action Artistique and the British Council, Victoria and Albert Museum, *Picasso and Matisse*, 1945
London: The London Gallery, *The Cubist Spirit and its Time*, 1947
London: The Arts Council, *Picasso, 55 Lithographs 1945–1947*, 1948
Lyons: Musée des Beaux-Arts, *Picasso*, 1953
Rome: Museo de Arte Moderna, *Picasso*, 1953
Milan: Palazzo Reale, *Picasso*, 1953
São Paulo: Museo de Arte Moderna, *Picasso*, 1954
Paris: Maison de la Pensée Française, *Picasso, Œuvres des Musées de Léningrad et de Moscou, 1900 à 1914*, 1954
Paris: Maison de la Pensée Française, *Picasso, Deux périodes, 1900–1914 et 1950–1954*, 1954
Paris: *Musée des Arts Decoratifs, Picasso 1900–1955*, 1955
Munich: Haus der Kunst, *Picasso 1900–1955*, 1955
London: The Arts Council, *Picasso: Fifty Years of Graphic Art*, 1956
New York: Museum of Modern Art, *Picasso: 75th Anniversary Exhibition*, 1957
Paris: Galerie Louise Leiris, *Picasso, Peintures 1955–56*, 1957
Arles: Musée Réattu, *Picasso, Dessins, Gouaches, Aquarelles 1898–1957*, 1957
Philadelphia: Museum of Art, *Picasso*, 1958
Paris: Galerie Louise Leiris, *Picasso: Les Ménines 1957*, 1959
Marseilles: Musée Cantini, *Picasso*, 1959

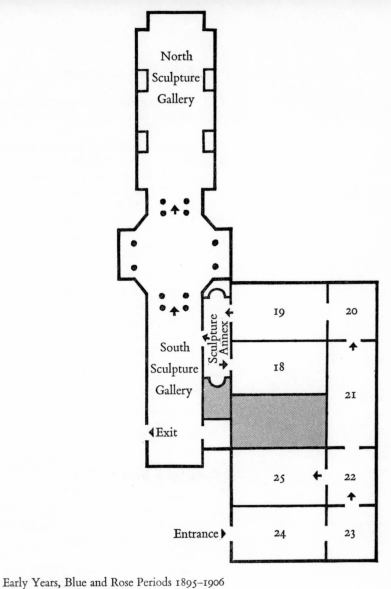

Plan of Exhibition

Catalogue Notes

In the dimensions height precedes width.
Where a picture is included in Zervos' *catalogue raisonné* (see bibliography) the reference is given after the measurements and inscription. [z]

Until 1898 Picasso always signed pictures with his father's name (Ruiz) as well as his mother's (Picasso). In 1898/9 he began occasionally to use his mother's name only, but from 1900/1 onwards he dropped his father's name from his signature.

Between 1907 and 1914 the signature was no longer on the face of the canvas but could often be found on the back. The reason for this was that during the early cubist period both Picasso and Braque sought to express the anonymity of the painter by refusing to sign on the picture itself. In later years at the request of dealers and collectors Picasso signed on the front of many of these paintings. It has been a habit with him throughout his life not to sign a picture until it leaves his studio, with the result that many paintings were signed several years after they were finished. Not infrequently, and in particular since 1925, he has dated his canvases with the day, month and year, and in recent years he has sometimes added the dates of each day that he has worked on the painting.

Malaga, 1881–91
Corunna, 1891–5
Barcelona, 1895–1904
Visits:
1895, September, Madrid
1897, summer, Malaga
    autumn and winter, Madrid
1898, Horta de San Juan, province of
    Tarragona
1900, October–November, Paris
1900–1, new year, Malaga
1901, spring, Madrid
    May–December, Paris

During his early childhood in Malaga Picasso showed an overwhelming desire to express himself by drawing and painting. He was encouraged by his father who earned a modest living as an artist and teacher of art. Paintings made in Corunna at the age of 14 show extraordinary accomplishment and a year later he began to find his place among the artists and poets of Barcelona, immersed in a *fin de siècle* atmosphere. His early dedication to the arts combined with his unusual talent led Picasso to explore wider fields and seek new influences. These he found in Paris. In 1900, the year of his first visit, he was deeply impressed by the Parisian verve of Toulouse-Lautrec, the exoticism of Gauguin and the powerful expressionism of Van Gogh. With eagerness and insight he readily assimilated what appealed to him in their styles without forgetting what he had learnt in his native country from El Greco, Velázquez and Goya. His life in Barcelona, where his family helped to alleviate his painful struggle against poverty, and some months spent in Madrid, kept alive the Spanish elements in his work.

Corunna, 1895   *Plate 4a*

1 Girl with Bare Feet

Oil on canvas: 29½ × 19½ in. (75 × 50 cm.)
Signed top right: *P. Ruiz*
z.i.3
Lent by the artist

Picasso painted this picture at the age of 14 – a small masterpiece which owes much to the great tradition of Spanish painting. It is also prophetic of the beggars of the Blue period in its ascetic severity, and of the colossal nudes of the early 'twenties in the massive heaviness of the hands and feet.

Barcelona, c.1897   *Plate 4b*

2 Interior of Tavern

Oil on canvas: 7 × 9½ in. (17·8 × 24·2 cm.)
Unsigned
z.vi.101
Lent by the O'Hana Gallery, London

In spite of the academic training which his father imposed on him, Picasso was conscious at an early date of other styles of painting, which he had seen reproduced in magazines. Compare Daumier, Forain and particularly the early work of Van Gogh.

Barcelona, 1899   *Plate 4c*

3 Portrait of the Artist's Sister

Oil on canvas: 59 × 39½ in. (149·8 × 100·3 cm.)
Signed bottom left: *P. Ruiz Picasso*
z.i.377
Lent by the artist

One of Picasso's favourite models at this period was his sister Lola. In these early days he was intrigued by seeing reproductions of the work of the Pre-Raphaelites and Whistler.

Paris, autumn 1900   *Plate 1b*

4 Le Moulin de la Galette

Oil on canvas: 35 × 45¾ in. (89 × 116·2 cm.)
Signed bottom right: *P. R. Picasso*
z.i.41
Lent by Mr and Mrs Justin K. Thannhauser, through the Thannhauser Foundation, New York

Probably the first painting done by Picasso in Paris. On his arrival Picasso was fascinated by scenes of

Parisian bourgeois life. The *Moulin de la Galette* is a popular dance hall in Montmartre. The influence of Toulouse-Lautrec is apparent. (Compare *Au Moulin-Rouge – La Danse*, Toulouse-Lautrec, 1890.)

Paris, 1900 *Plate 4e*

5 Head of a Woman

Oil on canvas: 14 × 13 in. (35·5 × 33 cm.)
Signed left: *P. Ruiz Picasso*
Z.I.27
Lent by the Hon. Michael Astor

This delicately painted head shows Impressionist influences, particularly that of Toulouse-Lautrec.

1901 – 4   Blue Period

Barcelona, 1901–4
Paris, 1904–
Visits:
1901, May–December, Paris
1902, October–early 1903, Paris

During his visit to Paris in 1900 Picasso had found inspiration chiefly in the bright colour and the gay bourgeois life seen in cabarets, public gardens and on the racecourse. On his return in the spring of 1901, after a few months in Madrid, his mood had changed and an element of melancholy, intensified by pervading cold ethereal blue tones, began to dominate his work. The subject matter was chiefly drawn from vagabonds, beggars and prostitutes, the victims of society who frequented the bars of Montmartre or the streets of Barcelona. The greater part of these years was spent in Barcelona, where he found daily in the streets the pathetic figures of blind beggars or poor women bowed compassionately over their children. Allegories concerning poverty, blindness, love, death and maternity were often in his thoughts, particularly when he was working on large compositions, and the figures, more sculptural in form than in the previous period, are given dramatic emphasis by the simplicity of their backgrounds. It has been said that at this time he was influenced by the Catalan painter Nonell. The Blue period marks a deliberate step towards a plastic representation of form and emotional subject matter and hence away from the atmospheric effects of the Impressionists.

Barcelona, spring 1901 *Plate 4d*

6 Bullfight

Oil on board mounted on panel: 19½ × 25½ in. (49·5 × 64·7 cm.)
Signed bottom right: *Picasso*
Z.VI.378
Lent by Mr Stavros S. Niarchos, St Moritz

In this period Picasso painted several bullfight scenes, working not during or immediately after the fight, as might be expected, but in advance, in order to pay for his ticket. They are all brilliant in colour and show a strong contrast between the sunlight and shadow. This is probably the most dramatic in its content. The dying horse, prophetic of *Guernica* (see note to cat. no. 143), draws attention to the foreground, but the asymmetric composition centres round the bull, silhouetted against the sunlit side of the arena, giving a remarkable sense of space by unconventional means.

Paris, 1901   *Plate 4j*

7 Auteuil Races

Oil on board: 18×28 in. (45·5×71 cm.)
Signed bottom left: *Picasso*
Lent by Mr Lee Hardy, London

Adding to the scenes of Parisian life in cafés and
parks Picasso painted several racecourse landscapes
(see z.vi.301). In the brilliance of the colour and the
movement of the crowds this is one of the most
animated versions.

Paris, 1901   *Plate 2a*

8 The Mourners

Oil on canvas: 39⅜×35½ in. (100×90 cm.)
Signed bottom right: *Picasso*
z.i.52
Lent by Mr Edward G. Robinson, Beverly Hills

In the early spring of 1901 the poet Casagemas, who
had accompanied Picasso to Paris, committed sui-
cide. This painting is an allusion to the young
painter's sorrow at the loss of his friend. A similar
group of figures appears in the lower half of a larger
composition known as *Evocation* or *The Burial of
Casagemas*, now in the Petit Palais, Paris (z.i.55).
The treatment of the figures shows a tendency to
abandon Impressionist techniques for a more sculptural interpretation of form.

Paris, 1901   *Plate 2b*

9 Dwarf Dancer (La Nana)

Oil on canvas: 40⅛×23⅝ in. (102×60 cm.)
Signed bottom left: *Picasso*
z.i.66
Lent by the Museum of Modern Art, Barcelona

A resemblance to the 'pointillist' technique of Seurat
may be noticed, but the technique is used by Picasso
without a systematic observance of divisionist
theories. The speckled brilliance of the dress and
background serves to give movement to the figure.
With characteristic disregard for systematic rules the
painting of the face and limbs, however, shows only
slight deviation from the earlier Impressionist
tradition.

Paris, 1901   *Plate 4J*

10 On the Upper Deck

Oil on cardboard mounted on panel: 19⅜×25¼ in.
(49·2×64·2 cm.)
Signed bottom right: *Picasso*
*Lent by the Art Institute of Chicago (Mr and Mrs L. L.
Coburn Collection)*

Picasso was impressed by the gaiety of Parisian life,
not only by night but also in the public gardens, on
the boulevards and at the racecourses. This painting
of the upper deck of the *bateau mouche*, the Parisian
water-bus, is surprising in the boldness of its composition. The triangle formed by the prow of the
boat placed off-centre sets up a contrast between the
intimacy of the figures in the foreground and the
remoteness of the houses on the distant *quai*.

Paris, 1901   *Plate 4h*

11 Blue Roofs

Oil on board: 15¾×23⅝ in. (40×60 cm.)
Signed bottom left: *Picasso*
z.i.82
Lent by the Visitors of the Ashmolean Museum, Oxford

Painted from the windows of the artist's studio,
130*ter* Boulevard de Clichy. Compare with this the
view (z.i.75), showing the trees and passers-by beneath the same windows. Both paintings show
strong Impressionist influence.

Paris, 1901   *Plate 4i*

12 Portrait of Gustave Coquiot

Oil on canvas: 39⅜×31⅞ in. (100×81 cm.)
Signed bottom right: *Picasso*
z.i.84
Lent by the Musée National d'Art Moderne, Paris

Picasso met Coquiot, a shrewd critic and enthusiastic
collector, at his first exhibition at the gallery of
Vollard in June 1901. He painted this portrait of him
and, a few months later, a second smaller portrait,
(Coll. Bührle, Zurich, z.i.85) which shows him
seated in front of paintings he had collected. In the
version exhibited here he is watching a cabaret show
which is reflected in the mirror behind him.

Paris, 1901   *Plate 1a*

13 Self Portrait

Oil on canvas: 32×22½ in. (81×60 cm.)
Unsigned.
z.i.91
Lent by the artist

During his first years in Paris Picasso lived in great
poverty. His first exhibition with Vollard in June

1901 was not a success, nor was an exhibition with Berthe Weill the following year. Privation and disillusionment are apparent in the sad, penetrating expression in this portrait.

Paris, 1901 *Plate 4g*

14 Child holding a Dove

Oil on canvas: $28\frac{3}{4} \times 21\frac{1}{4}$ in. (73×54 cm.)
Signed centre left: *Picasso*
z.1.83
Lent by the Dowager Lady Aberconway, London

Throughout his life Picasso has shown in his work a love of children and of doves. Here the essential charm of the subject which might have led to sentimentality has been rigorously balanced by the boldness of the brushwork, the heavy outlines and the suppression of contour modelling, characteristics which evoke the technique of Van Gogh and Gauguin. The vigorous treatment brings about a marriage of opposites between the technique and the subject.

Paris, 1901 *Plate 5a*

15 Mother and Child

Oil on canvas: $35\frac{3}{4} \times 23\frac{5}{8}$ in. ($91 \cdot 5 \times 60$ cm.)
Signed centre left: *Picasso*
z.1.109
Lent by Mr and Mrs William Goetz, Los Angeles

This theme which recurs at intervals throughout Picasso's life is often found in the paintings of the Blue period (see z.1.107, 108, 110, 111, 115, 117).

Barcelona, 1902 *Plate 5b*

16 Two Women at a Bar

Oil on canvas, $31\frac{1}{2} \times 36$ in. ($80 \times 91 \cdot 4$ cm.)
Signed top left: *Picasso*
z.1.132
Lent by Mr Walter P. Chrysler, Jr, New York

Throughout the Blue period Picasso found his models among the outcasts, prostitutes, beggars and drunkards who stood at street corners and frequented cafés. In this painting he conveys the misery of the two women without even showing their faces.

Barcelona, 1903 *Plate 5e*

17 Street in Barcelona

Oil on canvas: $23\frac{5}{8} \times 15\frac{3}{4}$ in. (60×40 cm.)
Signed bottom right: *Picasso*
z.1.122
Lent by the Hon. Michael Astor

Picasso spent most of his early years living in towns with visits to the country during the summer months. His landscapes in consequence are often seen from the windows of his studio placed high up in the building and overlooking roof tops or the long perspective of the streets below. This picture shows the view from his attic studio in Barcelona, just as the *Blue Roofs* of 1901 (cat. no.11) shows the houses across the street in Paris; many years later the *Café at Royan* (cat. no.163) was painted in the same way.

Barcelona, 1903 *Plate 6b*

18 The Blind Man's Meal

Oil on canvas: $37\frac{1}{2} \times 37\frac{1}{4}$ in. ($95 \times 94 \cdot 5$ cm.)
Signed top right: *Picasso*
z.1.168
Lent by the Metropolitan Museum of Art, New York (Gift of Mr and Mrs Ira Haupt, 1950)

Throughout his life Picasso has often dwelt on the tragedy of blindness. During this period in particular there are many paintings of blind beggars (cf. *The Old Guitarist*, 1903, Art Institute of Chicago, z.1.202, and *The Old Jew*, 1903, Museums of Leningrad and Moscow, z.1.175), and the subject of blindness appears also in the splendid etchings, *The Frugal Repast*, 1904 (Geiser, pl.2), and those of the blind Minotaur of 1934 (Geiser, pls.86–88).

Here, with his characteristic sensitivity in the treatment of the hands, Picasso indicates how the sense of touch can be a substitute for the sense of sight.

Barcelona, 1903 *Plate 6a*

19 The Soler Family

Oil on canvas: $59 \times 78\frac{3}{4}$ in. (150×200 cm.)
Signed top left: *Picasso*
z.1.203 and 204
Lent by the Musée des Beaux-Arts, Liège

The tailor Soler was a friend of Picasso in Barcelona and was willing to make him suits in exchange for paintings. In addition to this family group, which recalls in its realism the group portraits of Courbet, the tailor earned fine portraits of the same period of himself (z.1.199), and Señora Soler (Coll. J. Thannhauser, New York, z.1.200). The background of the family group is known to have gone through several

Girl writing, 1934, 63⅞ × 51⅜ in.   *Mr and Mrs Samuel A. Marx* (136)

changes. The background was originally left bare by Picasso and was painted in by a friend who encircled the family in a wooded grove (z.i.204). Nearly ten years later Kahnweiler bought the painting and on seeing it again Picasso objected to the background and decided to repaint it. His first course was to cover the trees with cubist rhythms related to his current style but this also failed to satisfy him and he finally painted it over with the present uniform background which enhances the importance of the figures.

Barcelona, 1903   *Plate 3a*

20 La Vie

Oil on canvas: 77⅜ × 50⅞ in. (196·5 × 129·2 cm.)
Signed top left: *Picasso*
z.i.179
Lent by the Cleveland Museum of Art (Gift of Hanna Fund)

As in some earlier paintings such as *Science and Charity*, 1896, and the *Burial of Casagemas*, 1901 (z.i.55), this picture has an allegorical quality though the meaning is somewhat obscure. Love, disillusionment and maternity are suggested in turn in the naked couple on the left, the two drawings that form the background, and the draped woman and child on the right. Two standing figures clasping each other occur in many paintings and sketches of this period (cf. *The Embrace*, 1900, Museums of Leningrad and Moscow, z.i.26), and the theme of maternity recurs frequently, but to find them together in a composition to which has been added the two studies of crouching nude couples is unique. The device of placing pictures within a picture has a suggestion of the *collage* technique of the cubist period; it recurs frequently in later years, particularly in recent work. Barr calls this 'a "problem" picture, awkward but with a serious statuesque dignity.' (Barr, p.26).

Paris, 1904   *Plate 5d*

21 Portrait of a Woman

Tempera on cardboard: 40 × 29¾ in. (101·6 × 75·5 cm.)
Signature not authentic
z.i.215
Lent by the Matthiesen Gallery, London

This is a portrait of the wife of the actor Harry Baur.

1904–6   Saltimbanque and Rose Period

Paris
Visits:
1905, summer, Holland
1906, summer, Barcelona and Gosol,
         Lérida (Spanish Pyrenees)

In 1904 Picasso finally moved to Paris. He took a studio in the *Bateau Lavoir,* a building inhabited by painters and poets, high up on the slopes of Montmartre. The more spirited and bohemian atmosphere of his new friends, and the company of the beautiful Fernande Olivier, led him away from the melancholy subjects which had obsessed him during the Blue period. With frequent visits from Max Jacob, Apollinaire and Salmon his studio became known as the '*Rendezvous des Poètes*'. It was here that the famous banquet in honour of the Douanier Rousseau took place in 1907.

The paintings of the Blue period had at last begun to sell to dealers and collectors such as Gertrude and Leo Stein, Wilhelm Uhde, and the Russian, Shchukine. The actors and strolling players of the boulevards and circuses became his friends and found their way into his paintings in tender nostalgic association. Harlequin, who had always been a favourite character in Picasso's imagination, made frequent appearances in his compositions, often figuring as a portrait of the artist himself. The predominant blue of the preceding year gave way to gentle tones of pink and grey.

The paintings of 1904 are often recognizable by elongations of the limbs that recall the mannerist style of El Greco, but by 1905 Picasso had abandoned these distortions for a classical purity of proportion. This in turn gave way to an insistence on sculptural qualities with a predominant emphasis on volume.

During these years Picasso paid a brief visit to Holland. He spent the summer of 1906 at Gosol, in the Pyrenees, where he painted many portraits, studies of Spanish peasants, and compositions. On his way to Gosol he had paid a visit to his family in Barcelona and refreshed his memories of the Romanesque and Gothic art of Catalonia. Even more important to him at this time was the discovery of Iberian sculpture dating from pre-Roman times, examples of which had been recently acquired by the Louvre. They attracted him by their unorthodox proportions, their disregard for refinements and their rude barbaric strength. These influences rapidly gained an important place in his work, and led to the sculptural distortions of nudes painted on his return to Paris in the autumn of 1906. During these years Picasso produced his first pieces of sculpture (*The Jester*, 1905 z.i.322, *Head of Fernande*, 1905 z.i.323; *Girl combing her Hair*, 1906 z.i.329, etc.), also a remarkable series of etchings (*The Frugal Repast*, 1904, Geiser, pl.2, *The Saltimbanques*, 1905 Geiser, pl.7; *Salome*, 1905, Geiser, pl.9, etc.)

Paris, *c.*1905   *Plate 5g*

22   Woman in a Chemise

Oil on canvas: 28⅝ × 23⅝ in. (72·5 × 60 cm.)
Signed and dated bottom left: *Picasso/05*
z.i.307
Lent by the Tate Gallery, London

Picasso paid frequent visits to the Louvre and was familiar with Greek, Egyptian and Etruscan art. In this painting, as in the *Girl with a Fan*, 1905 (cat. no.26), the severity of the pose suggests Egyptian bas-reliefs. There is a feeling of detachment in the freshness of a newly discovered classicism and an idyllic simplification of form.

Paris, 1905   *Plate 5c*

23   Girl with a Basket of Flowers

Oil on canvas: 59⅞ × 25¾ in. (152 × 65 cm.)
Signed top right: *Picasso* inscribed; on the back: *Picasso/13 rue Ravignan/1905*
z.i.256
Lent from a private collection, Paris

The model was a young flower seller who posed for other artists, including Modigliani. This painting was exhibited at the first post-Impressionist exhibition at the Grafton Galleries in London in 1910.

Paris, 1905   *Plate 5f*

24   Boy with Pipe

Oil on canvas: 39⅜ × 32 in. (100 × 81 cm.)
Signed bottom left: *Picasso*
z.i.274
Lent by the Hon. and Mrs John Hay Whitney, London – New York

As the melancholy of the Blue period melted into a more serene and gentle mood Picasso found new inspiration in the circus folk and travelling players. In this painting of a young actor the background with its floral design recalls in gentler terms the method of Van Gogh of using an ornamented background close behind his sitter.

Schooredam, Holland, summer 1905   *Plate 5h*

25 Dutch Girl

Blue chalk, gouache and oil on cardboard, mounted on panel: 30¾ × 26½ in. (78 × 67·3 cm.)
Inscribed top left: *a mi querido amigo/Paco Durio Picasso/1905 Schoart*
z.i.260
Lent by the Queensland Art Gallery, Brisbane

One of the few paintings made by Picasso during the few weeks spent in Holland with the Dutch writer Schilperoort. It is prophetic of the colossal nudes painted in the early 1920's (see *Two Seated Women*, 1920, cat. no.94), but it had a more immediate effect in guiding Picasso to his first serious work in sculpture. Paco Durio, to whom the painting was given, was a Spanish sculptor and ceramist, formerly a friend of Gauguin. He lived near Picasso in Montmartre and helped him materially in his early days of poverty.

Paris, 1905   *Plate 3b*

26 Girl with a Fan

Oil on canvas: 39½ × 32 in. (99 × 81·3 cm.)
Signed bottom right: *Picasso*
z.i.308
Lent by the Hon. and Mrs W. Averell Harriman, New York

See note to *Woman in a Chemise* (cat. no.22). This is one of the most masterly and graceful examples of Picasso's first classical period.

Paris, 1905   *Plate 5i*

27 Girl with Pitcher

Oil on canvas: 39⅜ × 32 in. (100 × 81 cm.)
Signed bottom right: *Picasso*
z.i.330
Lent by Mr Edward James, London

After the poetic misery of the Blue period, with its emaciated figures had given way to the gentler melancholy of the harlequins and 'saltimbanques', the basic colours of Picasso's work changed to pinks, ochres and greys, and for a time the anatomy in his nudes revealed a graceful classicism.

Paris, 1905   *Plate 5j*

28 Boy and Horse

Watercolour on paper, mounted on panel:
19⅝ × 12⅝ in. (50 × 32 cm.)
Signed top left: *Picasso*
z.i.270
Lent by the Tate Gallery, London

This is a study for a large picture *Boy leading a Horse* 1905 (Coll. Wm. S. Paley, N.Y., z.i.264). The same boy with the horse appears also in the central section of *The Watering Place*, 1905 (z.i.265), a study made presumably for a large scale composition.

Gosol, 1906 (previously dated 1905)   *Plate 7a*

29 La Toilette

Oil on canvas: 59½ × 39½ in. (151 × 100 cm.)
Signed top left: *Picasso*
z.i.325
Lent by the Albright Art Gallery, Buffalo

The classical influences of which Picasso had become conscious and which tended to eliminate the fragile 'gothic' anatomy of the Blue period, culminate in this painting where the idyllic grace of the figures recalls the goddesses of ancient Greece.

Paris, 1906   *Plate 10b*

30 Self Portrait

Oil on canvas: 35½ × 27½ in. (90 × 70 cm.)
Signed and dated bottom left: *Picasso/1906*
z.i.375
Lent by the Philadelphia Museum of Art (A. E. Gallatin Collection)

During the early years Picasso frequently made self portraits as drawings and paintings. This, however, is the last but one *painted* by him. The last is dated 1907 (see z.ii*8). The portrait exhibited was painted in Paris, probably on his return from Gosol. The influences of pre-Roman Iberian sculpture are evident in the treatment of the head. The clear-cut features and the forcefully drawn eyes have a direct, almost primitive, quality which derives from these early works of art.

Paris, 1906   *Plate 10a*

31 Nude

Oil on canvas: 41 × 31¼ in. (105 × 79 cm.)
Signed top right: *Picasso*
z.i.344
Lent by M Jacques Ulmann, Paris

Paris, 1906

32 Seated Female Nude

Oil on canvas: $59\frac{1}{2} \times 39\frac{3}{8}$ in. (151×100 cm.)
Signed top left: *Picasso*
z.i.373
Lent by the National Gallery, Prague

Plate 7b

Picasso's desire to represent sculptural form is here admirably realized. There are other paintings of the same model (see z.i.366, 367, 374 etc.) but this is one of the most monumental of this period. It is a forerunner of the colossal nudes of the early 'twenties (see cat. no.94).

1907 – 9

Transition – The Negro Period

Paris
Visits:
1908, summer, La Rue-des-Bois, near Creil (Oise)
1909, summer, Horta de San Juan, province of Tarragona, Spain

During the summer of 1906 Picasso met Matisse at the house of Leo and Gertrude Stein. Matisse had been acclaimed as the leader of the Fauve movement and his great picture, *La Joie de Vivre*, had been exhibited that spring at the *Salon des Indépendants*. Picasso, who at that time refused to exhibit in large group exhibitions, was nevertheless highly conscious of the revolutionary violence in the paintings of the Fauves, and held Matisse, Derain and Braque in great esteem. However, their tendency to insist in their work on the sole importance of colour appealed to Picasso no more than did the search for representation of atmospheric effects practised by the Impressionists. At the same time there were other influences at work. The painting of Cézanne had become familiar to him through the dealer Ambroise Vollard who had given him his first exhibition in Paris in 1901. Cézanne's search for a valid interpretation of form and the geometric basis of his compositions had impressed the young Spaniard who desired to create a tangible, three-dimensional quality in his painting. Picasso had also discovered the greatness of an obscure old man, the Douanier Rousseau, the fresh vitality of whose work corresponded to Picasso's desire to discover new forms of expression. These were the years when the spontaneity of primitive art imported from Africa and the South Seas was beginning to be noticed by certain painters in Paris, and styles which had formerly been despised as barbaric began to be recognized as possessing great emotive power.

On his return from Gosol in the autumn of 1906, Picasso had continued to emphasize and simplify form, especially in his paintings of nudes; but it was not until that winter that he was to start work on a large canvas which was to be a turning-point not only in his own career but also in the history of contemporary art. In the same spring he had painted *The Harvesters* (cat. no.33), a picture which shows more than any other a use of colour similar to that of the Fauves and also a desire to create movement in a composition. Both these tendencies were used in this case at the expense of a more penetrating sense of form. But in the great picture *Les Demoiselles d'Avignon* (cat. no.34), his aim had changed. Colour was strictly limited to pinks and blues and forms became clearly defined and static. For many months he had prepared great quantities of studies and he continued his ideas in 'postscripts' long after the painting had been left unfinished. This painting became the testing-ground for doubts that had troubled him. With a courage which greatly perturbed his friends, he sacrificed all the charm, bordering at times on the sentimental, which had built up an early fame. In his search for more powerful forms of expression he had become conscious of the vitality of primitive art and his recent visit to Catalonia had renewed his desire to recapture at all costs its fundamental qualities. The result was a great picture which was greeted by cries of horror from his most enlightened friends and which was left rolled up in his studio for more than twenty years, but which was to be an overwhelming influence in the future.

The period which followed *Les Demoiselles* began with paintings which developed out of the treatment of the two figures on the right of the painting. Their similarity to African sculpture, which had that year become one of Picasso's sources of inspiration, has led to the adoption of the term Negro period for the months that followed. The new style depended in particular on a simplification of form and a clarification of the methods by which it was depicted. With a disregard for classical tradition, distortions were used freely to emphasize volume and convey emotional sensation. Picasso applied his discoveries with great consistency to all the subjects that presented themselves to him: the human form, flowers, landscapes, portraits or still life.

In the summer of 1908 Picasso spent a few weeks in the country north of Paris, using his new style to paint landscapes. On his return he was surprised to find that Braque, with whom his friendship had begun a year earlier, had also independently followed a similar course in the south of France. It was these paintings by Braque which were first given the name 'cubist' by the critic Vauxcelles when they were exhibited a few months later.

During the following summer at Horta de San Juan Picasso developed the principles of his new style still further. The clear-cut rocky landscape gave him the opportunity to pursue Cézanne's recommendation that nature should be considered in terms of the cylinder, the sphere and the cone, a principle which he applied with equally astonishing results to portraits and to still life.

Paris, spring 1907 *Plate 8b*

33 Harvesters

Oil on canvas: $25\frac{5}{8} \times 31\frac{7}{8}$ in. (65×81 cm.)
Signed bottom left: *Picasso*
z.ɪɪ*2
Lent from a private collection, New York

This painting is perhaps unique in the way Picasso has used colour rather than form as a method of representation. It is close to Fauvism in this technique. In its agitated movement the composition resembles *Peasants and Oxen* (autumn 1906) now in the Barnes Foundation, Merion, Penn. (z.ɪ.384): a tendency that he was to abandon for a more static mood in compositions beginning with the *Demoiselles d'Avignon* (cat. no.34).

Paris, 1906–1907 *Colour frontispiece*

34 Les Demoiselles d'Avignon

Oil on canvas: 96×92 in. (244×233 cm.)
z.ɪɪ*18
Lent by the Museum of Modern Art, New York (acquired through the Lillie P. Bliss Bequest)

This important and much-discussed painting was the result of many drawings and composition sketches made during the winter of 1906/7 (see z.ɪɪ**632 –44). The picture itself was painted rapidly and was continued in many 'postscripts'. Barr suggests that the influence of Cézanne, apparent in the earlier sketches, was tempered by memories of El Greco's compact figure compositions and the angular highlights of his draperies, rocks and clouds. (Barr, p.54). The three figures on the left are closely related to the nudes painted during the previous year which show clearly the influence of primitive Iberian sculpture, but in contrast to them the two figures on the right show a new and disturbing influence. Their mask-like faces are given relief with bold hatching, unlike the features drawn with lines on a flat surface of the other women. It seems certain that the two right-hand figures were painted later than the others and that Picasso's newly-discovered enthusiasm for African masks from the French Congo had influenced him to give them a strong barbaric structure. Their ghoulish and sinister features make the already forbidding faces of their companions appear dignified and almost gentle.

In his revolt against Impressionism Picasso had gone further than the Fauve painters and was using such violent forms of expression that his friends, including Matisse, Braque and Derain, to whom he showed this painting, were unanimous in their condemnation. For many years the canvas remained rolled up in the studio. It was reproduced for the first time in *La Révolution Surréaliste* in 1925 and was never exhibited in public until 1937.

The title of the picture was given jokingly some years later by André Salmon, who pretended to see a resemblance between these ladies displaying their charms and the inmates of a brothel in the Carrer d'Avinyo (Avignon Street) in Barcelona. It is evident from the early studies that Picasso conceived the composition as a kind of allegory, which he later abandoned. Originally the central figure was a sailor surrounded by naked women, fruit and flowers, while from the side entered another sailor holding a skull. The sailors, however, have disappeared and there remain only the women with the fruit, grouped in the foreground so as to give a sense of hieratic authority to the figures.

Although the painting remained hidden for so long it assumed a legendary power in the minds of those who had seen it. Its strength can be ascribed not only to the bold incongruity of the faces but to the fact that it can be called the first cubist painting. The forms, broken and re-assembled in angular design, herald the geometric discipline of cubism, and the shallow depth against which they appear is an essential characteristic of the new style. But above all the painting owes its importance to the fact that it is the first in which Picasso became entirely himself and assimilated all influences so as to let his own genius triumph. It is the battlefield on which he won his own liberty.

Paris, spring 1907 *Plate 10a*

35 Jugs and Lemon

Oil on canvas: $21\frac{3}{4} \times 18$ in. ($55\cdot3 \times 45\cdot8$ cm.)
Unsigned.
z.ɪɪ*32
Lent by Mr Clive Bell, Sussex

Paris, summer 1907 *Plate 9a*

36 Dancer

Oil on canvas: $59 \times 39\frac{1}{2}$ in. (150×100 cm.)
Signed top right: *Picasso*
z.ɪɪ*35
Lent by Mr Walter P. Chrysler, Jr, New York

The vitality of African sculpture and the liberty with which it interpreted the human form impressed Picasso deeply. Unlike other painters who became admirers of primitive art but continued to paint in their former style, Picasso pried into the secrets of its strength and made them his own. In this picture the oval face clearly has its origin in negro masks

The angular background and the distortions of the figure form a complete unity which is moving towards the static and monochromatic paintings of early cubism.

Paris, 1907   *Plate 10e*

37 Negro Dancer

Oil on canvas: $24\frac{3}{4} \times 16\frac{7}{8}$ in. (63×43 cm.)
Signed top right: *Picasso*
z.ii★36
Lent from a private collection, London

A comparison between this painting and the *Dancer* of the same year (cat. no.36) reveals increased emphasis on physical distortions. The arms framing the head are treated as a schematic suggestion, the body is shrunk into a slender stem, but the crouching thighs are so enlarged as to suggest tropical fruit. The almond-shaped head painted with strong rapid brush-strokes remains the centre of interest.

Paris, summer 1907   *Plate 9b*

38 Flowers

Oil on canvas: $36\frac{1}{2} \times 28\frac{1}{2}$ in. (92×73 cm.)
Signed bottom left: *Picasso*
z.ii★30
Lent by Mr and Mrs Ralph F. Colin, New York

The discovery of the violent strength of negro sculpture came at a time when Picasso was preoccupied with the realization of solid forms on the two-dimensional surface of a canvas. He was thinking as a sculptor but acting as a painter. The flowers are here given such solidity that they suggest the possibility of making them into a construction in bronze but, as with the *Dancer* (cat. no.35), there is an inseparable unity between the object and its background.

Paris, winter 1907   *Plate 8a*

39 Nude with a Towel

Oil on canvas: $45\frac{5}{8} \times 35\frac{1}{2}$ in. (116×90 cm.)
Signed on the back: *Picasso.*
z.ii★48
Lent by La Vicomtesse de Noailles, Paris

The sculptural appearance of the figure, expressed in simple flat surfaces in which all detail is eliminated, gives it a 'barbaric' strength which is closely associated with the primitive vitality of African carvings. Picasso has succeeded in interpreting its emotional appeal in terms of Western art. The powerful simplicity of the form does not, however, eliminate a certain feeling of tenderness and uncouth charm.

La Rue-des-Bois, summer 1908   *Plate 10j*

40 Landscape [Not exhibited]

Oil on canvas: $39\frac{3}{4} \times 32$ in. (101×81 cm.)
Unsigned
z.ii★83
Lent from a private collection, Paris

During his brief visit to La Rue-des-Bois north of Paris, in the summer of 1908, Picasso was preoccupied with Cézanne's treatment of landscape. The desire to simplify form geometrically dominated his work. To achieve an impression of solidity and volume he adopted Cézanne's method of contrasting warm and cold colours on opposite facets of an object – reddish ochres opposed to bluish greens.

La Rue-des-Bois, summer 1908   *Plate 10h*

41 Landscape

Oil on canvas: $29 \times 23\frac{3}{4}$ in. ($73 \cdot 5 \times 60$ cm.)
Unsigned
z.ii★82
Lent from a private collection, Paris

See note to *Landscape*, 1908 (cat. no.40).

La Rue-des-Bois, summer 1908   *Plate 13b*

42 Landscape with Bridge

Oil on canvas: $31\frac{7}{8} \times 39\frac{3}{8}$ in. (81×100 cm.)
Signed bottom right: *Picasso*
Lent by the National Gallery, Prague

This painting clearly shows many characteristics of the birth of cubism: simplicity of form, elimination of detail, creation of three-dimensional effects and a continuity of forms joining each other without sharp breaks between them. The transition between the influence of Cézanne and the invention of a new style is clearly visible.

Paris, autumn 1908   *Plate 10f*

43 Landscape with Figures

Oil on canvas: $23\frac{5}{8} \times 28\frac{3}{4}$ in. (60×71 cm.)
Unsigned
z.ii★79
Lent by the artist

The influence of Cézanne may be felt in this painting but the unity of the figures with the landscape and its areas of light and shade confirm Picasso's knowledge of classical landscape painting of the 17th century. There is in existence a preparatory drawing (z.ii★66).

Paris, winter 1908   *Plate 12b*

44   The Bather

Oil on canvas: $51\frac{1}{4} \times 38\frac{1}{4}$ in. (130×97 cm.)
Signed top right (at a later date): *Picasso*
z.II*111
Lent from a private collection

The insistence on volume, treated in monochrome against a plain background, becomes increasingly evident during this period. In order to obtain a more complete conception, the form has been opened up, as it were, from behind so that both the back and the front of the body become visible, giving an exaggerated stereoscopic view. Picasso was painting what he knew to be there, rather than what can be seen from one fixed point of view.

Paris, winter 1908   *Plate 10c*

45   Male Nude

Oil on canvas: $36\frac{1}{4} \times 28\frac{3}{4}$ in. (92×73 cm.)
Signed top right (at a later date): *Picasso*
z.II*117
Lent from a private collection, France

The splendid statuesque simplicity of this nude constructed with no regard for detail finds its origins in negro sculpture. The body is built up of well-defined facets, and now abandoning Cézanne's method of contrasting warm and cold colours Picasso has achieved a sense of solidity by the use of monochromatic modelling.

Paris, winter 1908 or spring 1909   *Plate 12a*

46   The Fruit Dish

Oil on canvas: $29\frac{1}{4} \times 24$ in. (73×60 cm.)
Signed top right (at a later date): *Picasso*
z.II*121
*Lent by the Museum of Modern Art, New York,
(acquired through the Lillie P. Bliss Bequest)*

Here again the influence of the late Cézanne still life paintings can be felt in the folds of the napkin and the tilted plane of the table, which in this case is exaggerated so as to bring the background nearer to the main subject. The forms of the fruit are closely knit and framed by the arabesque of the white dish.

Paris, summer 1909   *Plate 10i*

47   Bust of a Woman

Oil on canvas: $28\frac{5}{8} \times 23\frac{5}{8}$ in. (73×60 cm.)
Signed bottom right (at a later date): *Picasso*
z.II*143
Lent by the Tate Gallery, London

The uncompromising strength and economy with which the forms are blocked in suggest the influence of African wood carvings.

Horta de San Juan, summer 1909   *Plate 13a*

48   The Reservoir

Oil on canvas: $23\frac{5}{8} \times 19\frac{3}{4}$ in. (60×50 cm.)
Unsigned
z.II*157
Lent from a private collection, Paris

The landscapes painted during Picasso's visit to Horta in 1909 are closely related to the severity of the arid mountains rising from the fertile plain. Simplified angular forms of houses, rocks and stone walls are grouped into compact units which are characteristic of pre-cubist tendencies.

Horta de San Juan, summer 1909   *Plate 38*

49   Portrait of Pallarès

Oil on canvas: $26\frac{3}{4} \times 19\frac{1}{2}$ in. (68×49.5 cm.)
Inscribed top left: *A mi queridisimo amigo Pallares/
Recuerdo de su amigo Picasso*
Lent by the Saidenberg Gallery, New York

Manuel Pallarès was a close friend of Picasso in his youth. They had stayed together on Pallarès' father's property at Horta de San Juan in the valley of the Ebro as early as the summer of 1898. This portrait was painted at the time of a second visit in 1909. It shows in monochrome Cézanne's method of constructing form with bold simplifications and a disregard for detail. Compare with this the portrait of Clovis Sagot (z.II*129).

1910 – 12   **Analytical Cubism**

Paris
Visits:
1910, Cadaquès (Costa Brava) with
    Derain and Fernande Olivier
1911, Céret (Pyrénées-Orientales) with
    Braque and Fernande Olivier

'I paint objects as I think them, not as I see them.' This remark made by Picasso to the poet Ramon Gomez de la Serna explains the essential divergence between Picasso and Cézanne. The latter had drawn his inspiration primarily from his immediate visual reaction to the objects before him. Picasso was increasingly drawn to making creations according to his own internal vision. In African art he had found a conceptual art which, in the same way, was not based on immediate visual reactions to a model. The original impact had been violent. It had forged the first real link between African art and Western ideas and it was followed during the two years that succeeded the painting of the *Demoiselles d'Avignon* by a growing tendency to bring order into these first impulses.

In close association with Braque, 'roped together like mountaineers', as Braque expressed it, Picasso began to clarify and systematize a new conception of the painter's experience. In order to understand form and interpret its existence on a flat surface they felt it necessary to break into the form, separate its elements, penetrate beneath the surface and become conscious of that which cannot be seen because accidentally it is at the back of the object in question. The appearance of an object taken from one point of view was manifestly insufficient. It should be conceived from all angles. They painted what they *knew* to be there. To do this effectively certain limitations seemed desirable. For a time both Braque and Picasso severely limited their palettes to sepia and grey with the occasional intrusion of an olive-green or ochre. Secondly, the traditional rules of linear perspective were completely abandoned, and modelling in the round gave place to flat crystalline facets which, built up together, gave the appearance of solid form. The system depended also on a close relationship between the figures or objects and their background. A sense of homogeneity throughout the picture was created by uniting the background closely with the objects so as never to allow a rift to appear between them. Each facet overlaps or touches its neighbour, giving an appearance both of a solid architectural construction and of the translucence of crystal. The fervour with which the two creators of cubism developed their discoveries led them into a language of abstractions. Their work became more purely conceptual and increasingly detached from normal visual appearances. For a while they preferred not even to sign their works, so as to give them a sense of detachment, even impersonality; as a result it is sometimes not easy to distinguish their work at this period.

It would be a mistake, however, to see in these works purely impersonal abstract design. In every case they are based on the conception of some definite object, as well as the personality of the artist. Clues are always to be found. A symbolic moustache gives the clue to the face in which it may be the only recognizable feature.

The curve of a guitar or the stem of a glass is a guide to the identity of objects that have been shattered and rebuilt as an integral part of the picture. The eye as it travels over the picture finds itself above, behind, and in front of the object at the same time, but the movement is in the consciousness of the spectator rather than in the object itself. All these varied aspects are woven together into a new realization of the totality of the object.

Paris, spring 1910   *Plate 11c*

50 Head of a Woman

Oil on canvas: $25\frac{1}{4} \times 20\frac{1}{4}$ in. ($64 \cdot 2 \times 51 \cdot 5$ cm.)
Signed top left: *Picasso*
z.II*219
Lent from a private collection, London

Paris, spring 1910   *Plate 14b*

51 Portrait of Uhde

Oil on canvas: $30\frac{3}{4} \times 22\frac{3}{4}$ in. (81×60 cm.)
Unsigned
z.II*217
Lent from a private collection. London

In the portrait of Pallarès (cat. no.49), and also in the portrait painted in the same year of Clovis Sagot (Museum of Hamburg), the influence of Cézanne remains apparent, but in 1910 Picasso applied a more radical form of cubism to portrait painting. Following a light-hearted, almost grotesque portrait of Braque (1909, z.II*219) he painted three portraits of friends which became successively more analytical and abstract in style. The first of these, the portrait of Ambroise Vollard (Museums of Leningrad and Moscow, z.II*214), is a remarkable likeness in spite of its rigorous cubist technique. The same quality is present in the second, this portrait of the collector and critic, Wilhelm Uhde. But in the third, the portrait of Kahnweiler (Coll. Mrs Gilbert Chapman, New York, z.II*227), the likeness, in spite of numerous sittings, has succumbed to the uncompromising organization of form into the broken facets of analytical cubism. The portrait exhibited here has the same crystalline formation as that of Kahnweiler, in which the head is closely linked with its background and has a similar monochromatic treatment.

Paris, spring 1910   *Plate 14*

52 Girl with a Mandolin

Oil on canvas: $39\frac{1}{2} \times 29$ in. (100×73 cm.)
Signed and dated (since 1921) bottom right:
Picasso/10; signed on the back: *Picasso*
z.II*235
Lent from a private collection, New York

Although Picasso at this time relied very little on the actual presence of a model, this painting, like the portraits of 1910, is an exception. The name of the model was Fanny Tellier. Although the principle of the breaking up of form into facets in order to reconstitute a new reality is used in general, there are concessions to a system of modelling in the round in the arms and the breast which do not, however, interfere with the general harmony. With wilful ambiguity the head can be seen either as a solid block or as a flat surface linked by a transparent shadow to its background. In spite of a revolutionary technique the picture combines in masterly style the classical qualities of graceful poise, serene proportions, well-ordered composition and subtle variations of tone. Although Picasso has often stated that he considers this picture to be unfinished, it is perhaps the most complete in its achievement of all cubist paintings of the analytical period.

Paris, spring 1910   *Plate 11*

53 Nude

Oil on canvas: $36\frac{1}{4} \times 28\frac{3}{4}$ in. (92×73 cm.)
Signed and dated bottom left: *Picasso*/9
z.II*201

Lent by the Tate Gallery, London

By the spring of 1910 the new language of cubism was developing fast. The dissection of form and its reconstruction had become a masterly process which now led to a method of creating a new reality expressed in monochrome. The deep cavernous greens which appear in the background to this seated figure were to become increasingly rare in the paintings which followed, and the form of the body which here is still recognizable as a compact mass was later to be resolved into a schematic scaffolding constructed with powerful angular rhythms. (See *Nude, Cadaqués, cat. no. 54*). For a note on the date of this painting see: *Tate Gallery Catalogue; Foreign Paintings, Drawings and Sculpture*, London, 1959.

Cadaqués, summer 1910   *Plate 11a*

54   Nude

Oil on canvas: 73¼ × 23⅝ in. (186 × 60 cm.)
Signed bottom left (considerably later): *Picasso*
z.ii★233
Lent from a private collection

Picasso spent the summer of 1910 at Cadaqués, Spain, at the home of his friends the Pichots; Fernande Olivier and Derain were with him. The great paintings of this period become increasingly 'hermetic'. Their colour is consistently limited to browns and greys and the forms are organized in shallow depth over the entire surface of the picture so as to avoid sudden rifts. The eye travels from one facet to another over a continuous play of semi-transparent recessions and intrusions, occasionally picking up landmarks such as an eye, a breast, the line of the spinal column or a foot, and in its passage it can continually enjoy moving over surfaces that are convincingly definite and that create a reality of their own. The architecture of the human form reappears as a transparent scaffolding in which the interior and exterior are both apparent.

Paris, winter 1910/11   *Plate 11e*

55   Still Life with Books and a Bottle

Oil on canvas: 15 × 18¼ in. (38 × 46 cm.)
Signed on the back: *Picasso*
z.ii★241
Lent by Miss J. E. Norton, London

*c.*1911   *Plate 11d*

56   Glass and Straws

Watercolour on paper, 12 × 10¼ in. (30·5 × 26 cm.)
Unsigned
Lent from a private collection, Paris

In most cubist paintings of this period the denial of colour results in a luminosity which radiates from the painting itself. Light appears to emanate from the forms rather than to be projected from an exterior source.

Paris, spring 1911   *Plate 11f*

57   The Mandolin Player

Oil on canvas: 39⅜ × 27½ in. (97 × 70 cm.)
Signed on the back: *Picasso*
z.ii★270
Lent by M Fernand Graindorge, Liège

This is an excellent example of analytical cubism in its most hermetic stage. The pyramidal construction of the figure is composed of facets among which it is still possible to detect clues to the subject matter; but its essential merit lies in the freedom with which forms have been reorganized in an abstract manner.

Paris, spring 1911   *Plate 11h*

58   Soldier and Girl

Oil on canvas: 45¾ × 32 in. (116 × 81 cm.)
Signed top right: *Picasso*; signed on the back: *Picasso*
z.ii★254
Lent from a private collection, Paris

It is unusual to find two figures combined in a cubist composition of this period. Here the composition is in consequence less concentrated than usual towards the centre of the canvas. Clues to the subject matter are a moustache, epaulettes and badges of rank which distinguish the man, while the girl's presence is recognizable by her breasts.

Paris, spring 1911   *Plate 11g*

59   Table, Glasses, Cups, Mandolin

Oil on canvas: 24½ × 19½ in. (61 × 50 cm.)
Signed on the back: *Picasso*
z.ii★262
Lent by Lady Hulton, London

All cubist paintings have as their starting point a definite subject and it is always possible to find some reference to the original theme. Here the fringe round the edge of the table, the stems of glasses and the handle of a mug give clues.

Céret, summer 1911   *Plate 15a*

60   Man with a Pipe

Oil on canvas, oval: 36⅞ × 23⅜ in. (93 × 72 cm.)
Signed top right (many years later): *Picasso*
z.ii★★738
Lent from a private collection

Between 1911 and 1914 some thirty-five oval pictures were painted by Picasso. Braque also favoured the same form. They both found this shape particularly suited as a frame to their analytical cubist paintings which were based on a central mass of rhythmic rectangular constructions. This type of composition, which is of ancient origin, and derives from the almond-shaped *vesica piscis* of Byzantine art, leads to a suppression of the four corners of the rectangle. The enclosing oval also helps to give a three-dimensional effect to the whole picture, since the oval can be considered as a circular plane seen in perspective.

Synthetic Cubism

Paris
Montrouge, 1916–18
Visits:
1912, Avignon and Céret, later Sorgues (Vaucluse) with Eva (Marcelle Humbert), Braque and Mme Braque
1913, summer, Céret, with Eva
1914, summer, Avignon, with Eva, Braque and Derain, until the outbreak of war

In their enthusiasm during the first heroic years of cubism, Picasso and Braque carried this style, which had metaphysical as well as visual significance, to a degree of purity which threatened to make it a completely hermetic art. By the autumn of 1911 their analysis of form had led them to a point where all signs of the presence of the object itself had become difficult to trace. It became necessary to form a new link between painting and reality. Picasso had on several occasions demonstrated his love for his new companion, Eva (Marcelle Humbert), by introducing the letters of her name or the inscription *J'aime Eva* into his paintings, as a lover might carve initials in the bark of a tree. This addition, which might seem irrelevant, brought a new reference to reality into work otherwise verging on abstraction. Braque also had felt the same need. Having been trained by his father, a *peintre-décorateur*, in the techniques of painting *trompe l'œil* surfaces of marble and grained wood, he now introduced these into his work. Short-cutting Braque's painted imitations Picasso carried the idea further by taking a piece of oilcloth on which a pattern of chair-caning had been realistically reproduced (cat. no.61), and sticking it to the canvas itself.

From this followed rapidly the use of newspaper, wallpapers or any other ready-made material which could serve the dual purpose of becoming part of the composition and adding its own reality to the picture. This addition of foreign materials applied to the canvas itself was a revolutionary step, breaking the tradition established since the Renaissance, when painters abandoned the medieval embellishments in gilt relief and insisted on a unity of material throughout the picture.

The new technique (*papier collé*) proved to be an important discovery. It enabled Picasso to work with great rapidity, sometimes pinning scraps of coloured or patterned paper on to his work and varying their positions as he desired. In the *Still Life with Chair Caning* (cat. no.61), the first painting in which Picasso used this new technique, the letters JOU, part of the word '*Journal*', are painted next to a glass which has all the characteristics of the earlier analytical devices of cubism. Both of them are situated close to the piece of oilcloth which simulates chair caning; thus they have various meanings and create varying degrees of deception, a device which has been described as a visual pun. The austerity of hermetic abstractions had given way to a light-hearted self criticism.

Another development was the return to colour, or rather coloured surfaces, which could, by their action on the eye, give a sensation of depth. The former system of gradations in tone which created crystalline facets tended to give way to simple flat or textured planes. Texture, it was found, could also be used to differentiate between areas: it could put them on different planes and had the effect of a new method of perspective. The textures were in some cases created with sand, and in others simulated a 'pointillist' technique. By 1913 the monochromatic effects of early cubism had been abandoned; colour assumed a new role: it glowed from flat, evenly coloured and clearly defined areas and had no relationship to the Impressionist use of colour to create atmosphere.

A cubist painting was becoming an object in its own right; a tendency which brought Picasso to experiment in the creation of bas-relief constructions which were halfway between painting and sculpture.

During the early years of cubism, Picasso had devoted himself entirely to discoveries which led towards abstraction, but already in 1915 he began again to make drawings and some paintings (see *Head of a Young Man*, 1915, cat. no.83) in which he showed again his extraordinary talent for conventional representation. Drawings of his friends, Max Jacob, Vollard, and Apollinaire, made during the war, have the assurance and purity of line of drawings by Ingres.

Paris, 1911/12   *Plate 11i*

61 Still Life with Chair Caning

Oil, oilcloth and paper on canvas, with rope surround, oval: $10\frac{5}{8} \times 13\frac{3}{4}$ in. (27×35 cm.)
Unsigned
z.II*294
Lent by the artist

The cubist paintings of 1911 had developed into a hermetic system of great purity which bordered on abstraction. In this small work Picasso has taken the first steps towards a new link with reality. A piece of oilcloth, convincingly simulating chair caning, has been pasted on the canvas and above it are painted a wineglass and a lemon with uncompromising cubist analysis. Next to them are the three first letters of the word '*Journal*' – a humorous comment on the varying types of reality which can be introduced into the same picture. Picasso states that this is the first painting in which he used those methods which were to lead to the *papiers collés* of the succeeding years.

Céret, spring 1912   *Plate 18b*

62 The Bottle of Vieux Marc, Glass and 'Le Journal'

Charcoal and *papier collé* with pins on paper: $24\frac{5}{8} \times 18\frac{1}{2}$ in. ($62 \cdot 5 \times 47$ cm.)
Signed on the back: *Picasso*
z.II*334
Lent by Dr Henri Laugier, Paris

With audacity Picasso began to explore the possibilities of *collage* technique in the summer of 1912.

The use of scraps of material which already carried with them their own identity, such as pieces of wallpaper or newsprint, in a lightly-sketched drawing, brought important results – a confrontation of different conceptions of reality, an *ad hoc* introduction of colour and a clear definition of form. The use of 'ready-made' elements also served to give anonymity to the work and avoid the easy seduction of the dextrous handling of paint. It demonstrated that the work of art does not depend on rich materials and elaborate techniques. The artist becomes a magician who can transform commonplace material in his desire to achieve complete expression. Picasso had learnt from his father the technique of pinning cutouts to a painting as a temporary means of trying out an idea, but he now used it as a more direct means of creation and considered the results not as studies, but as finished pictures.

Paris, spring-summer 1912   *Plate 16a*

63   Spanish Still Life

Oil on canvas, oval: 18⅛×13 in. (46×33 cm.)
Signed on the back: *Picasso*
z.II*301
Lent from a private collection, France

The letters introduced into this picture are all parts of Spanish words: note the letter addressed to Don . . . (Barcelona), the letters SOL and SOMB ('sun' and 'shade') referring to a bullfighting revue, and CIDAD, part of the word '*Publicidad*'. This painting was reproduced by Apollinaire in the first book on cubism, *Les Peintres Cubistes* (Paris, 1913).

Sorgues, summer 1912   *Plate 15b*

64   The Aficionado

Oil on canvas: 53¼×32½ in. (135×82 cm.)
Inscribed on the back: *Portrait d'homme, Sorgues, 1912. Picasso*
z.II**362
Lent by the Kunstmuseum, Basel

Painted at Sorgues near Avignon, this painting reveals in many ways Picasso's continued interest in the bullfights which took place in the nearby arena at Nîmes. In the foreground we find the newspaper *Le Torero* and beside it a banderilla, while the figure of the 'aficionado' (bullfight fan) is constructed with solid shapes which evoke the Roman architecture of the arena and the narrow streets of a Provençal town. The composition is more evenly spread over the canvas in a rectangular pattern than in the paintings of the previous year (see *Man with Pipe*, cat. no.60).

Paris, winter 1912/13   *Plate 16b*

65   Bottle, Glass, Violin

Charcoal and *papier collé* on paper: 18½×24¾ in. (47×63 cm.)
Signed on the back: *Picasso*
z.II**405
Lent by M Tristan Tzara, Paris

The use of cut-out paper here has more than one purpose. On the left it indicates the shape of a bottle, whereas behind the glass and the violin it is used to create a sense of space; further to the right it imparts at the same time a shadow and a solidity to the body of the violin. The word '*Journal*' introduces a reference to a different kind of reality.

Paris, winter 1912/13   *Plate 16a*

66   Head of a Girl

Charcoal and *papier collé* on paper: 23¾×18½ in. (60×47 cm.)
Inscribed on the back: *Etude de tête de Jeune Fille Picasso*
Unsigned
z.II**402
Lent by M Tristan Tzara, Paris

This head should be compared with the head of the *Girl with a Mandolin* (cat. no.52). It expresses a similar conception executed with even greater economy of means.

Paris, winter 1912/13   *Plate 18a*

67   Still Life with Gas Jet

Oil on canvas: 27×21 in. (68·5×53 cm.)
Signed top left: *Picasso*; and on the back: *Picasso*
z.II**381
Lent from a private collection, London

Although this picture is a painting and not a *collage*, the technique of *papier collé* is evident in the flat planes and the use of sand to give texture. In addition to the clearly decipherable shapes of the guitar, the glass and the bottle, an interesting clue to the subject-matter is the line drawing of the gas jet.

Paris, 1913?   *Plate 16c*

68   Head

Charcoal and *papier collé* on cardboard: 17⅛×13⅛ in. (43·5×33 cm.)
Unsigned
z.II**414
Lent from a private collection, London

In his analysis of the head it is seldom that Picasso arrived at a solution which is as near to complete abstraction as this, but in the intensity of its systematic disregard for 'reality' it achieves a quality near to madness, akin to those moments of illumination which provided grounds for the most fruitful researches of the surrealists. This *collage* once belonged to one of the founders of surrealism, André Breton.

Paris, spring 1913   *Plate 16e*

69 **Head of a Man**

Oil and charcoal on paper, laid on canvas: $24\frac{1}{4}\times$ $18\frac{1}{4}$ in. ($61\cdot5\times46\cdot4$ cm.)
Signed top left (later): *Picasso*
z.II**431
Lent by Mr Richard S. Zeisler, New York

This painting, formerly belonging to Roger Fry, was one of the earliest cubist paintings to be bought by an English collector.

Paris, spring 1913   *Plate 16g*

70 **Violon au Café**

Oil on canvas, $31\frac{7}{8}\times21\frac{1}{4}$ in. (81×54 cm.)
Inscribed on the back: *Sur une table/un violon/un verre/une bouteille 1913 Picasso.*
z.II**438 *bis*

Lent by M Siegfried Rosengart, Lucerne

With the return to colour applied in large flat surfaces, and to more easily recognizable clues – seen here in the characteristic shapes of the violin – the most hermetic developments of analytical cubism begin to disappear and a new synthesis of form comes into being.

Céret, 1913   *Plate 16f*

71 **Harlequin**

Oil on canvas: $34\frac{3}{4}\times18\frac{1}{4}$ in. ($88\cdot5\times46\cdot5$ cm.)
Signed bottom right (considerably later): *Picasso*
Signed on the back: *Picasso*
z.II*333
Lent by the Municipal Museum, The Hague

This picture is dated in Zervos as spring 1912 but the construction of the face relates it to two drawings of the following year (see z.II**393 and 425). The composition of vertical bands is found in the work of the years 1912 to 1916, but it resembles closely the treatment in *Still Life with a Gas Jet* (cat. no.67) and the *Violon au Café* (cat. no.70).

Paris, autumn 1913   *Plate 19b*

72 **Woman in an Armchair**

Oil on canvas: $58\frac{1}{4}\times39$ in. (148×99 cm.)
Inscribed on the back: *Picasso Paris 1913*
z.II**522
Lent by Dr Ingeborg Pudelko Eichmann, Florence

This picture has been much reproduced and is known by various titles. It is a painting of great importance in the development of cubism and was also acclaimed by the surrealists as a marvellous example of 'fantastic art.' There is a study closely related to it (see z.II**785), and there are others made during the following year that are significant in their appeal to the subconscious. New and disquieting relationships between abstraction and sensuality and between dream and reality become apparent. Paul Eluard wrote of this painting: 'La masse énorme et sculpturale de cette femme dans son fauteuil, la tête grande comme celle du sphinx, les seins cloués sur la poitrine, contrastent merveilleusement – et cela ni les Egyptiens, ni les Grecs, ni aucun autre artiste avant Picasso n'avaient su le créer – le visage aux traits menus, la chevelure ondulée, l'aisselle délicieuse, les côtes saillantes, la chemise vaporeuse, le fauteuil doux et confortable, le journal quotidien.' (P. Eluard, *A Pablo Picasso*, Geneva, Paris, 1944, p.36.) Zervos reproduces seven drawings closely related to this painting: (z.VI.1259–61, 1263, 1265–7).

Paris, winter 1913/14   *Plate 16h*

73 **Student with Pipe**

Oil, sand, and *papier collé* on canvas: $28\frac{3}{4}\times23\frac{1}{4}$ in. (73×59 cm.)
Unsigned
z.II**444
Lent from a private collection, Paris

In order to give depth Picasso made use of various textured surfaces, such as crumpled paper and sand, and suggested roughness by using dots such as are often found on wallpapers and which can also be related to a 'pointillist' technique (see cat. nos.74, 77, 79, and 81).

Paris, 1914   *Plate 16j*

74 **Guitar, Skull and Newspaper**

Oil on canvas: $17\frac{3}{8}\times24$ in. ($43\cdot5\times61$ cm.)
Signed on the back: *Picasso*
z.II**450
Lent from a private collection, France

The tendency in synthetic cubism to flatten out volume and ignore space is well illustrated here. The use of surfaces decorated with wood graining or marbling is derived from the pasted wallpapers of *collage* technique. There is a macabre touch of humour in the curly wig with which the skull is decorated. It recalls the abundant black hair often seen in the early portraits of Picasso's Catalan friend Sebastian Junyer.

1914 *Plate 17c*

75 Still Life

Painted wood with upholstery fringe: $10 \times 18\frac{7}{8}$ in. ($25 \cdot 5 \times 48$ cm.)
Unsigned
Lent from a private collection, London

In 1912 Picasso began to explore the possibilities of three-dimensional constructions. The effect of *collage* had been to reduce the modelled facets of analytical cubism to the more two-dimensional effect of large flat planes, but the introduction of ready-made patterns, playing cards and crumpled paper brought with it the concept of the picture as an object in its own right as well as an illusion to the senses. During the two years that followed he produced a series of constructions in relief, the majority of which have since been destroyed. They were not accompanied by any production of sculpture in the round except for a polychrome bronze (*Le Verre d'Absinthe*, 1914, z.II**581–4), of which each of the six casts made was painted differently by Picasso.

Paris, 1914 *Plate 16i*

76 Glass and Dice

Black chalk, gouache and *papier collé* on paper laid on cardboard: $9\frac{1}{2} \times 6\frac{1}{4}$ in. (24×16 cm.)
Unsigned
z.II**501
Lent by M Heinz Berggruen

In all cases where newspaper was used in *collage* the colour of the wood pulp has changed, but the yellowing of the paper is of little importance to the composition and may in some cases add a richness to the general effect.

Paris, 1914 *Plate 17a*

77 Playing Card, Fruit Dish, Glass

Charcoal and *papier collé* on paper: $24 \times 18\frac{3}{4}$ in. ($61 \times 47 \cdot 5$ cm.) z.II**504
Lent from a private collection

In this excellent example of synthetic cubism, composed of large flat planes, the glass on the right is broken up in the manner of analytical cubism.

Paris, 1914 *Plate 17*

78 Fruit Dish, Guitar, Bottle

Oil on canvas: $36\frac{1}{4} \times 29$ in. (92×74 cm.)
Signed bottom left: *Picasso*
z.II**529
Lent from a private collection

Paris, 1914 *Plate 17*

79 Guitar, Playing Card, Glass, Bottle o Bass

Oil on canvas: $18\frac{1}{8} \times 21\frac{5}{8}$ in. (46×55 cm.)
Formerly signed on the back: *Picasso*; now relined
z.II**527
Lent by M César de Hauke, Paris

The inscription '*Ma Jolie*', which recurs in som twelve other paintings executed from 1912 to 1914 is a reference to a song which was popular at tha time; it was also an expression of Picasso's love fo Eva – Marcelle Humbert – whose name appears ir many cubist pictures, often with the inscriptior '*J'aime Eva*' or '*Jolie Eva*'. On 12 June 1912 he wrot to Kahnweiler: ' . . . I love her very much and I shal write her name on my pictures.' The 'pointillist' technique may have had its origin in wallpapers used ir *collage* (see *Playing Card, Fruit Dish, Glass*, cat. no.77 and *Student with Pipe*, cat. no.73).

Avignon, 1914 *Plate 18*

80 Seated Man with a Glass

Oil on canvas: $93 \times 64\frac{1}{2}$ in. (236×164 cm.)
Signed bottom right (later): *Picasso*
z.II**845
Lent from a private collection

The results of freedom gained by the use of *papie collé* are apparent in this picture, in which the *collag* process is imitated in paint. The body of the man is playfully distorted: one arm crosses the painting from left to right as a snakelike ribbon finishing in a minute oval on which the fingers are indicated, while the other arm holding the glass has the shape of a small flag. There is a drawing which closely resembles this painting (z.II**844). The audacious light-hearted distortions and the interplay of *collage* and painting in this picture are not uncommon at this period. Another admirable example is *Portrai of a Young Girl*, 1914 (Coll. Georges Salles, z.II** 528).

Paris, 1915 *Plate 19a*

81 Man Leaning on a Table

Oil on canvas: 78× 52 in. (200× 132 cm.)
Signed bottom right: *Picasso*
z.ii**550
Lent from a private collection

During the early years of the war Picasso worked for a long time on two canvases of which this is one. The serenity of their proportions and the grandeur of their composition place them among the highest achievements of synthetic cubism. Compare the *Guitar Player* (National Museum, Stockholm, z.ii** 551). An earlier state of this picture can be seen in the background of a photograph of Picasso in his studio in the Rue Schoelcher, Paris in 1915 (c.a.25, no.2, 1950).

Paris, 1915 *Plate 17e*

82 Still Life in a Landscape

Oil on canvas: 24½× 29½ in. (62× 75 cm.)
Signed top left (in 1952): *Picasso*
z.ii**541
Lent by M Heinz Berggruen

There are paintings of this period which show Picasso's intention of introducing a sense of depth by the association of landscape with cubist painting. This was in the nature of an experiment and there are photographs of his studio showing canvases with areas of landscape which were later painted out (see c.a.25, no.2, 1950). The idea of a still life combined with a distant horizon was developed, however, in the series with the theme of a table set in front of an open window (see cat. nos.90 and 92).

Paris, 1915 *Plate 17d*

83 Head of a Young Man

Oil on wood: 10× 7¼ in. (25·5× 18·5 cm.)
Signed and dated bottom right: *Picasso/1915*
z.vi.1281
Lent by Mrs Louise R. Smith, New York

During the heroic early years of cubism Picasso concentrated entirely on the discoveries he was making, but after the outbreak of war in 1914 he began to adopt once again a more representational style without, however, giving up the achievements which had widened the limits of painting. In 1915 he made careful and extremely skilful pencil drawings of his friends, and also made studies of fruit. The scope of the art of painting is vast and Picasso shows in this admirable small-scale portrait, painted when cubism had become established as a new visual language, that he did not intend to restrict himself entirely to one style.

Paris, late 1915 *Plate 20a*

84 Harlequin

Oil on canvas: 72¼× 41⅜ in. (183·5× 105·5 cm.)
Signed and dated bottom right: *Picasso/1915*
z.ii**555
Lent by the Museum of Modern Art, New York (acquired through the Lillie P. Bliss Bequest)

In the same year as the *Head of a Young Man* (cat. no.83) Picasso painted this new version of an old and favourite subject, Harlequin. In the quiet gaiety of its colour and the simplicity of its form it announces the greatest achievements of synthetic cubism, which were to culminate in the *Three Musicians* (cat. no.97) and the great still lifes of 1924–5. It marks the beginning of a period sometimes known as the Crystal period – a term given by Maurice Raynal – during which his work, though never austere, is ordered by a supple and accomplished discipline.

1917–24 **Cubism and Classicism**

Montrouge, 1916–18
Paris, 1918
Visits:
1917, spring, Rome, Naples, Florence
   summer, Madrid, Barcelona

   12th July 1918, Marriage to
   Olga Koklova

During the years of the war Picasso suffered not only from the dispersal of his friends but also from the death of Eva in the winter of 1915–16. Although he never ceased to paint and to develop the discoveries of cubism, his production during these years was less prolific. In the spring of 1917 he was persuaded by Jean Cocteau to go with him to Rome and design scenery and costumes for the ballet *Parade*, which was to be presented in Paris that summer. This expedition brought Picasso into contact with a new *milieu* and his visit to Italy revived his delight in classical forms and awakened a new interest in the *commedia dell'arte*. It was here that he met the young ballerina Olga Koklova, whom he married in the following year.

On his return to Paris his work showed frequent references to classical subjects, and the portraits of his beautiful young wife again show his consummate skill in representational painting. However, the achievements of cubism were never abandoned and he continued to develop this style with increasing strength. It culminated in two great canvases, variations on the same subject, *The Three Musicians*, painted in 1921 (cat. no.97). The other version is in the Philadelphia Museum of Art. As a parallel to the cubist paintings, Picasso made many paintings of female figures, nude or with classical drapery: see *Two Seated Women*, 1920 (cat. no.94). He emphasized the fullness of their forms, endowing them with a sense of fertility and mother-hood. Whatever dimensions he used for the actual size of the canvas, these figures always suggest monumental proportions: see *Nude Seated on a Rock*, 1921 (cat. no.96) and *The Race*, 1922 (cat. no.100).

In 1921 Olga gave birth to a son and Picasso's work reflected at once his preoccupation with this event. Motherhood (see *Mother and Child*, 1921 or '22 (cat. no.98) became a dominant theme in his painting in the neo-classical style.

With the renewed possibility of travelling during the summer months after the war, Picasso paid visits to the Mediterranean. During these years a subject which was repeated with many varia-tions was a table laden with objects standing before an open window: see *Table in Front of a Window*, 1919 (cat. no.90), and *Window opening on to the Rue de Penthièvre*, 1920 (cat. no.92). Familiar objects such as the guitar, the bowl of fruit and wine bottles con-tinued to be the chief elements in a series of still life paintings. After passing through a variety of moods, Picasso arrived at some of his major triumphs in the great canvases of 1924 and 1925: see the *Fish Net*, 1925 (cat. no.111). In these the techniques of cubism are used in a masterly way; the objects and their shadows interlock in great harmonious compositions, brilliant in colour and poetic invention.

Rome, spring 1917 — *Plate 20b*

85 L'Italienne

Oil on canvas: $58\frac{5}{8} \times 39\frac{3}{4}$ in. (149×101 cm.)
Inscribed top left (later): *Picasso/Rome 1917*
Z.III.18
Lent from the E. G. Bührle Collection, Zürich

This painting of uncompromising purity of style was painted in Rome while Picasso was working on his designs for the ballet *Parade*. It is evident that he was influenced by the Italian climate in the colour, and by traditional costumes associated with the *commedia dell'arte*.

Barcelona, summer 1917 — *Plate 17i*

86 Harlequin

Oil on canvas: $46\frac{1}{8} \times 35$ in. (117×89 cm.)
Unsigned
Z.III.28
Lent by the Museum of Modern Art, Barcelona

Picasso painted this picture during a short tour in Spain with the Russian Ballet; the tour included Madrid and Barcelona.

Paris, 1918 — *Plate 21b*

87 Harlequin

Oil on canvas: $57\frac{3}{4} \times 26\frac{1}{8}$ in. ($146 \cdot 5 \times 66$ cm.)
Signed bottom right: *Picasso*
Z.III.159
Lent by Mr and Mrs Joseph Pulitzer, Jr, St. Louis

In contrast to the *Harlequin* painted the previous year (see cat. no.86), this painting is an example of how Picasso can treat the same subject in very different ways. In this case, what has been lost from the point of view of conventional representation is more than recompensed by the strength of the composition and the inventions of form and colour.

Paris, 1918 — *Plate 17g*

88 Harlequin with a Guitar

Tempera on wood: $13\frac{3}{4} \times 10\frac{5}{8}$ in. (35×27 cm.)
Signed and dated bottom right: *Picasso/1918*
Z.III.158
Lent by M Heinz Berggruen

This small, exquisitely handled painting is an illustration of Picasso's ability to work on a miniature scale as well as in vast dimensions.

Paris, Montrouge 1918 — *Plate 22a*

89 Guitar

Oil and sand on canvas: $31\frac{7}{8} \times 17\frac{3}{4}$ in. (81×45 cm.)
Signed and dated bottom left (later): *Picasso 18*
Z.III.140
Lent by the Rijksmuseum Kröller-Müller, Otterlo, Holland

This composition, admirably conceived in severe geometric terms, belongs to the Crystal period. The carefully controlled contrasts between smooth and sanded surfaces add a richness of texture. Compare *Guitar*, Museum of Modern Art, New York (Z.II** 570, erroneously dated winter 1916).

St. Raphaël, 1919 — *Plate 17h*

90 Table in Front of a Window

Gouache on paper: $12\frac{1}{4} \times 8\frac{3}{4}$ in. ($31 \cdot 8 \times 22 \cdot 2$ cm.)
Signed and dated bottom right: *Picasso/19*
Z.III.401
Lent by M Siegfried Rosengart, Lucerne

During his summer visits to the Mediterranean Picasso painted several pictures of this subject. The closed backgrounds of cubist still life and figure paintings have here given way to the perspective of an open window and the horizon beyond. Compare another version painted later in Paris, *Window Opening onto the Rue de Penthièvre* (cat. no.92).

Paris, 1919 — *Plate 22b*

91 Still Life on a Chest of Drawers

Oil on canvas: $31\frac{7}{8} \times 39\frac{3}{8}$ in. (81×100 cm.)
Unsigned
Z.III.443
Lent by the artist

As a parallel to the cubist pictures of this period, the 'realist' vein occupied an important place in Picasso's painting between 1917 and 1924.

Paris, 1920 — *Plate 21a*

92 Window Opening onto the Rue de Penthièvre

Oil on canvas: $31\frac{7}{8} \times 39\frac{3}{8}$ in. (81×100 cm.)
Z.IV.74
Lent from a private collection, New York

The long series of still lifes on a table in front of an open window culminated in this large canvas, impressive in its restrained colour and masterly in composition. The view of houses in the background is closely knit into the main subject. Compare an early version of the same subject (*Table in Front of a Window*, cat. no.90).

Juan-les-Pins, 1920 *Plate 17j*

93 Landscape

Oil on canvas: $20\frac{1}{2}\times27\frac{1}{2}$ in. (51×68 cm.)
Unsigned
Z.IV.107
Lent by the artist

Since the visit to Horta de San Juan in 1909, landscape paintings by Picasso are rare and all those painted before 1940 are small in size. It is interesting to note that at this early date the sun is given an almond shape, as in the false sun in *Guernica* (1937).

Paris, 1920 *Plate 24a*

94 Two Seated Women

Oil on canvas: $76\frac{3}{4}\times64\frac{1}{4}$ in. (195×164 cm.)
Signed bottom right: *Picasso*
Z.IV.217
Lent by Mr Walter P. Chrysler, Jr, New York

This great painting is one of the earliest and most impressive of Picasso's neo-classical style of the early 'twenties. The effect of ponderous anatomy appears in 1905 in the *Dutch Girl* (cat. no.25), and later, in more exaggerated form, in *Seated Female Nude*, 1906 (cat. no.32). Here the sculpturesque modelling is carried to an extreme which excludes all that might lead to sentimentality and gives a majesty and serenity to these gigantic figures.
cat.no.32).

1920 *Plate 26a*

95 The Rape

Tempera on wood: $9\frac{3}{8}\times12\frac{7}{8}$ in. (23×32 cm.)
Signed and dated bottom left: *Picasso/1920*
Z.IV.109
Lent by the Museum of Modern Art, New York (the Philip L. Goodwin Collection)

During the neo-classical period Picasso painted many small tempera panels of classical subjects, miniature tableaux of heroic scenes, with an ease which recalls the charm of Roman or Pompeian frescoes (see Z.IV.278).

1921 *Plate 26c*

96 Nude Seated on a Rock

Tempera on wood: $5\frac{7}{8}\times3\frac{7}{8}$ in. (15×10 cm.)
Unsigned
Z.IV.309
Lent by Mr James Thrall Soby, New Canaan, Conn.

This painting can claim to be the smallest and the most exquisite of the gigantic nudes.

Fontainebleau, 1921 *Plate 23*

97 Three Musicians

Oil on canvas: $79\times87\frac{3}{4}$ in. (201×223 cm.)
Inscribed bottom right: *Picasso/Fontainebleau/1921*
Z.IV.331
Lent by the Museum of Modern Art, New York (Mrs Simon Guggenheim Fund)

During the summer of 1921 at Fontainebleau Picasso painted two great canvases of the same subject, nearly the same size. The other version belongs to the Philadelphia Museum of Art (Z.IV.332). Both versions represent three masked carnivalesque characters seated at a table, a pierrot playing the clarinet, a harlequin violinist or guitarist and a monk. The dog lying under the table appears only in the New York version shown here. This monumental composition in the rigorous technique of synthetic cubism is rather like a showpiece of cubist invention wittily dressed in the disguises of the *commedia dell 'arte*. The flat coloured shapes, simple and in general rectilinear, become ideograms, significant of reality. The figures owe their monumental character not only to their massive block-like construction but also to the contrast made by the minute size of their spider-like hands. With humour and poetry Picasso has tempered the rigidity of a style which could have become merely decorative. His subject is gay but he gives his festive trio a solemn, even sinister, majesty.

1921 or 1922 *Plate 24b*

98 Mother and Child

Oil on canvas: $38\frac{1}{4}\times28$ in. ($97\cdot2\times71$ cm.)
Signed bottom left: *Picasso*
Z.IV.289
Lent by Mr and Mrs Alex L. Hillman, New York

With the exception of a portrait of Mme Paul Rosenberg and her daughter, dated 1918 (Z.III.242), the theme of 'Mother and Child' does not reappear in the work of Picasso after the Blue period until the birth of his son Paul in 1921. This fine composition, alive with action and full of robust human form, is the happiest achievement in a series which comprises at least twelve known variations (Z.IV.266, 286, 289, 299, 300, 311, 370, 371, 384, 455, and VI.1392, 1397).

1922   *Plate 26e*

99 Guitar on a Red Cloth

Oil on canvas: $32\frac{1}{8} \times 45\frac{7}{8}$ in. (81×116 cm.)
Signed and dated bottom right: *Picasso/22*
Z.IV.440
Lent from a private collection

A fine example of late synthetic cubism in which
rectilinear rhythms still dominate. The exuberant
clarity in the colour, the subject, and the treatment
of the fringed red cloth evoke inevitably a Spanish
atmosphere.

Paris, 1922   *Plate 26h*

100 The Race

Tempera on wood: $12\frac{7}{8} \times 16\frac{1}{4}$ in. ($32 \cdot 5 \times 41 \cdot 5$ cm.)
Unsigned
Z.IV.380
Lent by the artist

This design was used for the drop curtain of an
'opérette dansée', *Le Train Bleu*, produced in Paris
in 1924 by Serge Diaghilev, with book by Cocteau,
music by Darius Milhaud, and scenery by Henri
Laurens.

Dinard, 1922   *Plate 26b*

101 Still Life with a Guitar

Oil on canvas: $32\frac{1}{2} \times 40\frac{1}{2}$ in. ($83 \times 102 \cdot 5$ cm.)
Signed and dated bottom left: *Picasso/22*
Z.IV.418
Lent by M Siegfried Rosengart, Lucerne

Like many of the still life subjects painted in Dinard
during the summer of 1922, this picture shows
Picasso's use of areas shaded with a series of parallel
wavy lines which give a vibration not unlike the
light filtered through venetian blinds or reflected
from the rippled surface of water.

Dinard, 1922   *Plate 26d*

102 Fruit Dish, Bottle, Packet of Cigarettes

Oil on canvas: $14\frac{1}{4} \times 17\frac{3}{4}$ in. (36×45 cm.)
Signed bottom left: *Picasso*
Z.VI.1433
Lent by M Heinz Berggruen

See note to cat. no.101, *Still Life with a Guitar*.

Paris, winter 1922/3   *Plate 26f*

103 Woman and Child

Oil on canvas: $51\frac{1}{2} \times 38\frac{1}{4}$ in. (130×97 cm.)
Signed bottom right: *Picasso*
Z.IV.455
Lent by Mr Walter P. Chrysler, Jr, New York

This is a later example of the theme which preoccupied Picasso after the birth of his son in the
spring of 1921 (see *Mother and Child*, 1921 or 1922,
cat. no.98).

1923   *Plate 25a*

104 Pipes of Pan

Oil on canvas: $80\frac{1}{2} \times 68\frac{5}{8}$ in. ($204 \cdot 5 \times 174$ cm.)
Unsigned
Z.V.141
Lent by the artist

The strength of the modelling of the figures, the
suppression of all irrelevant detail, and the simple
grandeur of the composition give power and nobility
to this idyllic scene.

1923   *Plate 26g*

105 Seated Woman

Oil on canvas: $36\frac{1}{4} \times 28\frac{3}{4}$ in. (92×73 cm.)
Signed bottom left: *Picasso*
Z.V.3
Lent by the Tate Gallery, London

The seated female figure has been Picasso's most
inexhaustible source of inspiration. During the classical period there are many versions of this subject,
painted with a great variety of invention but always
expressing a sense of timeless immobility.

1923   *Plate 26i*

106 Woman Seated in a Red Chair

Oil on canvas: $39\frac{3}{8} \times 32$ in. (100×81 cm.)
Signed bottom right: *Picasso*
Z.V.140
Lent by Mr Edward James, London

See note on *Seated Woman* (cat. no.105). The freedom in the painting of this picture in comparison
with the more measured treatment of the other version of the same subject is an example of the significance of each variation in the work of Picasso which
gives each painting a unique quality.

1924   *Plate 26j*

107 Paul as Harlequin

Oil on canvas: 51⅛ × 38⅛ in. (130 × 97 cm.)
Unsigned
z.v.178
Lent by the artist

This portrait of the artist's son at the age of three is once more an example of Picasso's love of children, of fancy dress and festive occasions. There are several such portraits, in which Paul is dressed as Harlequin, Pierrot, or a toreador. This is one of the last paintings of Harlequin, a character which in early years appears often as a self-portrait, and which is here delegated to his son. Compare a cubist version painted in the same year (z.v.328).

Juan-les-Pins, 1924   *Plate 27a*

108 Landscape

Oil on canvas: 15 × 18⅛ in. (38 × 46 cm.)
Signed and dated bottom right: *Picasso/24*
z.v.332
Lent by M Heinz Berggruen

When moving to a new place, Picasso has nearly always made drawings, and often paintings, which give a vivid sense of the atmosphere of his surroundings. This landscape was painted during a visit to Juan-les-Pins in the summer of 1924.

Paris, 1924   *Plate 27c*

109 Still Life with Apples

Oil on canvas: 14⅞ × 21½ in. (37·5 × 54·5 cm.)
Signed and dated top right: *Picasso/24*
z.v.253
Lent by the Trustees of King's College, Cambridge

1925 – 35   **The Anatomy of Dreams**

Paris
Visits:
1925, spring, Monte Carlo
      summer, Juan-les-Pins
1926, Juan-les-Pins
1927, Cannes
1928, 1929 Dinard
1930, 1931 Juan-les-Pins

    1932, Buys Château de
           Boisgeloup at Gisors (Eure)

Visits:
1933, Cannes, Barcelona
1934, Boisgeloup, San Sebastian,
    Madrid, Toledo, Escorial,
    Barcelona
1935, Boisgeloup

The strong influence of classicism on Picasso revealed itself not only in classical figures and compositions but also in the order and purity of form which he had imposed on the great cubist paintings, mostly still life, up to 1925. In this year, however, a new torment that had begun to disturb his spirit revealed itself in the great canvas, *Three Dancers*, 1925 (cat. no.110). Here it is evident that the post-war hopes of a new Golden Age shared by so many had vanished, and yielded to a desperate ecstatic violence, expressive of frustrations and foreboding. This painting is the first to show violent distortions which have no link with the classical serenity of the preceding years. It heralds a new freedom of expression. During the following years the human form was to be torn apart, not with the careful dissection practised during the years of analytical cubism, but with a violence which has rarely been paralleled in the work of any artist. Picasso, however, not only decomposes and destroys, he invents new anatomies, new architectures and a new synthesis, incorporating the world of dreams with mundane reality. By this means he is able to bring about a metamorphosis, more powerful and more profound than the simple *trompe l'œil* effects produced with oil paint on canvas. The most unorthodox, and even the meanest of materials can be given a new life and a new significance by him and it is in this feat that Picasso has continually shown his poetic strength. In *Guitar*, 1926 (cat. no.113), with materials as uninviting as nails, wire, paper and a floorcloth, he has created a picture which can have a violent emotional effect.

Picasso readily understood the desire of his surrealist friends to look for inspiration in the workings of the subconscious, and he allowed his paintings to be shown with theirs in group exhibitions. His conviction that painting should be conceptual rather than purely visual had always led him to value the friendship of poets, and the close link in surrealism between poetry and painting appealed to him strongly. His early association with André Breton and his long friendship with Paul Eluard gave birth to a period fertile in inventions.

Never in the work of Picasso do we find that the expression of emotion overwhelms formal considerations. Never does it become uncontrolled expressionism. His remodelling of the human form is based on cubist discoveries: for instance, the placing of two eyes surprisingly in a face seen in profile, a familiar characteristic from 1935 onwards, springs clearly not only from emotional promptings but also from the cubist intention to see that which is hidden but is known to exist (see cat. no.138). Nor has he ever abandoned his desire to interpret three-dimensional solidity of form. His methods of doing so vary, however, from the use of flat surfaces and tenuous lines to conventional shading to indicate volume. In the late 'twenties Picasso returned to bas-relief and sculpture, often inventing forms which were interchangeable in either medium. The head on the right in the painting *The Painter and his Model*, 1928 (cat. no.117) was also made up by Picasso as a painted metal construction, and this process of producing the effects he desired alternatively in either medium has increased in more recent work.

In 1932, with the space afforded by large out-buildings at his recently acquired Château de Boisgeloup, Picasso was able to produce a series of important sculptures. Some were made in iron with the technical aid of the sculptor Gonzalez; others were large plaster heads inspired by a new model, Marie-Thérèse Walter, who appears frequently in paintings of this period: see *Woman in a Red Armchair*, 1932 (cat. no.128) and *The Mirror*, 1932 (cat. no.127). In 1935, Marie-Thérèse bore Picasso a daughter, Maïa.

But sculpture was not the only art beside painting which occupied Picasso in the early 'thirties. It was during this period that with great vigour he produced some of his most remarkable graphic work, illustrating many books, such as the *Chef d'Œuvre Inconnu* of Balzac and Ovid's *Metamorphoses*, and later (in 1937) the *Histoire Naturelle* of Buffon, as well as books by his friends the poets Tzara,

Eluard and others. In addition, Picasso himself found time to writ
many long poems, turbulent in form and violent in imagery. Thi
prodigious activity has been characteristic of Picasso throughou
his life, even during such years as these when he was undergoin
the serious emotional stress which culminated in his separation fron
his wife.

Monte Carlo, spring 1925   *Plate 28b*

110   Three Dancers

Oil on canvas: $84\frac{5}{8} \times 56\frac{1}{4}$ in. (215×140 cm.)
Unsigned.
Z.V.426
Lent by the artist

In this picture Picasso has brought into action a new,
disquieting sense of movement and the dislocation
of the human form which is prophetic of even more
violent expression in the future. It comes as a sudden
contrast to a painting such as *Girl with Mandolin*
(cat. no.112) painted in the same year. Before this,
distortion had been formal whereas it is here emotional and convulsive. In its sudden violence this
great painting is a turning-point in the art of Picasso.
It coincides with the early days of his close association with the surrealists and seems to echo André
Breton's dictum, 'Beauty must be convulsive or
cease to be'.

Juan-les-Pins, summer 1925   *Plate 25b*

111   The Fish Net

Oil on canvas: $39\frac{3}{4} \times 32\frac{5}{8}$ in. ($100 \times 82 \cdot 5$ cm.)
Signed and dated top right: *Picasso/25*
Z.V.459
Lent from a private collection, New York

This painting belongs to the great series of still lifes
painted between 1923 and 1926. The fish net itself
is drawn by scoring the dark paint and revealing a
lighter surface beneath.

1925   *Plate 27b*

112   Girl with Mandolin

Oil on canvas: $51\frac{3}{8} \times 38\frac{5}{8}$ in. (130×97 cm.)
Signed and dated bottom left: *Picasso 25*
Z.V.442
Lent from a private collection, New York

The tenuous line with which the features are drawn
is superimposed on the large flat surfaces familiar in
synthetic cubism. In contrast to the serenity of this
picture compare *Three Dancers* (cat. no.110).

1926   *Plate 27*

113   Guitar

Oil on canvas with string, *papier collé* and floorcloth
with two-inch nails, points outwards: $38\frac{1}{4} \times 51\frac{1}{4}$ in
(97×130 cm.)
Unsigned
Lent by the artist

In spite of its formal appearance, this picture bear
evidence of violent emotion comparable in intensity
to that of the *Three Dancers* (cat. no.110). The
use of commonplace materials such as a floorcloth
nails and string is a rude challenge to the fine manner
proverbially associated with art. In addition, Picasso
has described his original intention of inserting razor-
blades round the edge of the canvas to wound the
hands of anyone attempting to touch it. This mani-
festation of rage against society is balanced by the
metamorphosis that takes place in the picture itself
The materials, base and even harmful in themselves,
can become in the imagination, as the title suggests,
a musical instrument slung from a nail on the wall.
The picture has a poetic significance which far sur-
passes its formal qualities; yet it is due to them, and
to the surprising and humble nature of the materials
and the economy with which they are used.

1927   *Plate 27e*

114   Figure

Oil on wood: $51 \times 38\frac{1}{8}$ in. (130×97 cm.)
Unsigned
Z.VII.137
Lent by the artist

1927   *Plate 27f*

115   Woman Sleeping in a Chair

Oil on canvas: $36\frac{1}{4} \times 28\frac{3}{4}$ in. (92×73 cm.)
Signed and dated top left: *Picasso/27*
Z.VII.72
Lent by Betty Barman, Brussels

Picasso at this period had begun to take increasing
liberties in his rearrangements of the human form.
Monstrous distortions appear, but they always carry
with them a significance and an understanding of the

human condition. Features are displaced with extraordinary freedom, and in the process they gain a new emotional meaning.

Paris, 1927   *Plate 29a*

116   Seated Woman

Oil on wood: $51\frac{1}{8} \times 38\frac{1}{4}$ in. (130×97 cm.)
Signed and dated right: *Picasso/27*
Z.VII.77
Lent by Mr James Thrall Soby, New Canaan, Conn.

This awe-inspiring figure is one of the most remarkable and dignified solutions that Picasso has found for this often repeated theme. In the head, in particular, he shows his great ability in the creation of a mask.

1928   *Plate 29b*

117   Painter and Model

Oil on canvas: $51\frac{1}{2} \times 64$ in. ($130 \cdot 8 \times 162 \cdot 5$ cm.)
Signed and dated bottom left: *Picasso/28*
Z.VII.143
Lent by Mr Sidney Janis, New York

From 1926 onwards the relationship of the artist to his model became an absorbing subject for Picasso. It is magnificently illustrated in a series of etchings made in 1927 for the *Chef d'Œuvre Inconnu* of Balzac and for the *The Sculptor's Studio*, 1933-4, part of the so-called Vollard suite, and later in a series of lithographs of 1954. In this complex and ingenious composition, a face in profile appears surprisingly to be the least abstract element in the painting. The canvas separates the model on the left from the artist holding his palette on the right. At this period Picasso was again beginning to think in terms of sculpture and there is in existence a painted metal construction which corresponds to the artist's head. A somewhat simpler and early version of this painting is *The Studio* (Museum of Modern Art, New York, Z.VII.142).

Dinard, 21 August 1928   *Plate 27h*

118   Bathers with a Ball

Oil on canvas: $6\frac{1}{2} \times 8\frac{3}{4}$ in. ($16 \cdot 5 \times 22 \cdot 5$ cm.)
Signed and dated bottom left: *Picasso/28*; inscribed on the stretcher: *Dinard 21 août 28 no.1*
Z.VII.220
Lent from a private collection

During his second visit to Dinard, in the summer of 1928, Picasso painted a series of small brightly-coloured beach scenes in which the distortions of the human form are light-hearted and humorous (see Z.VII.218-227, etc.).

5 May 1929   *Plate 27g*

119   Woman in an Armchair

Oil on canvas: $76\frac{3}{4} \times 51\frac{1}{8}$ in. (195×130 cm.)
Dated on the back: *5 Mai xxix*
Z.VII.263
Lent by the artist

In his desire to recreate human anatomy, investing it with emotional significance, Picasso varies his interpretations. Sometimes they are composed with sculptural volumes (see *Woman Seated in a Red Armchair*, cat. no.126), but here the languid female form is contrasted with the rigid rectangular architecture of the room. The flat arabesque of the body grows like a plant from the chair, and carries her limbs like branches and her breasts as heavy fruit, in an eloquent combination of violence and tenderness.

26 May 1929   *Plate 27i*

120   Standing Bather

Oil on canvas: $76\frac{3}{4} \times 51\frac{1}{4}$ in. (195×130 cm.)
Dated on the stretcher: *dimanche XXVI mai XXIX*
Z.VII.262
Lent by the artist

In contrast with the gay dancing bathers of the Dinard period (see *Bathers with a Ball*, cat. no.118) this birdlike figure appears full of foreboding, static and sculptural.

1929   *Plate 32a*

121   Woman in Red Armchair

Oil on canvas: $25\frac{1}{2} \times 21\frac{1}{4}$ in. (65×54 cm.)
Signed and dated top right: *Picasso/XXIX*
Z.VII.294
Lent from a private collection, U.S.A.

From Picasso's idea of translating painting into sculpture sprang the more grandiose desire to build monumental structures based on an architecture inspired by the human form. There are several canvases of this period which were founded on this conception (see Z.VII.290-294).

1929   *Plate 27j*

122   Head

Oil on canvas: 29×24 in. (73×60 cm.)
Signed and dated top right: *Picasso 29*
Z.VII.248
Lent from a private collection, London

There is a marked contradiction in the duality of this head between the classical outline of the profile drawn in the background and the distorted features of a sharp-tongued monster superimposed on it. The profile, the same that appears in the *Painter and Model* (cat. no.117), is recognizable as a self-portrait.

Paris, 7 February 1930   *Plate 28a*

123   Crucifixion

Oil on wood: 20×26 in. (51×66 cm.)
Dated on the back: *7-II-xxx*
z.VII.287
Lent by the artist

During this period, deep emotional strain is evident in a series of drawings (see z.VII.279–283) which culminated in this painting of the crucifixion. This picture is unique among the paintings of Picasso, both in its subject and because of its symbolic imagery and involved composition. Many of the religious symbols connected with the crucifixion can be deciphered, in spite of abrupt changes of scale and astonishing violence in the distorted anatomies. The relevant drawings dating from 1927 are metamorphic in style. They are often closely related to the *Seated Bather* (cat. no.124). Later on, in 1932, Picasso returned to the theme of the crucifixion in a further series of drawings based on the Isenheim altar-piece of Matthias Grünewald. Many of these studies have elements which reappear in the great composition of 1937, *Guernica* (z.IX.65).

Early 1930   *Plate 31a*

124   Seated Bather

Oil on canvas: 64¼×51 in. (163·5×130 cm.)
Signed bottom right: *Picasso*
z.VII.306
Lent by the Museum of Modern Art, New York (Mrs Simon Guggenheim Fund)

There are many examples of Picasso's creation of new anatomies, extending from the series of bathers drawn at Cannes in 1927 (see z.VII.84–109), to sheets of studies of anthropomorphic constructions of 1933. These are built up of various elements which, by metamorphosis, become the components of anatomies. In this picture a bloodless monumental figure is pieced together with invented bonelike structures; a monstrous giantess has come to life in the light of a tender maritime dawn. There are other paintings of 'bone' figures also seen against a serene blue sky (see z.VII.300–305). They have in common with the sculptures Picasso was inventing at the same time an insistence on the hollow space enclosed by an outer scaffolding or shell.

Paris, 22 February 1931   *Plate 30*

125   Pitcher and Bowl of Fruit

Oil on canvas: 51¼×64 in. (130·2×162·5 cm.)
Signed and dated bottom left: *Picasso xxxi*; dated on the back
z.VII.322
Lent from a private collection, New York

There is a series of large still lifes painted in 1931 of which this is one of the finest. Although they are in many ways cubist they are composed with curvilinear rather than rectangular rhythms. In this painting the use of heavy black lines recalls medieval stained glass and accentuates the effect of light, which seems to emanate from within the picture. This technique is related to the linear sculptures made of metal rods which Picasso had invented as early as 1928.

1932   *Plate 32*

126   Woman Seated in a Red Armchair

Oil on canvas: 51¼×38¼ in. (130×97 cm.)
Unsigned
Lent by the artist

This painting, with its powerfully defined volumes, is closely related to sculptures executed by Picasso at Boisgeloup in 1931 and 1932. A sketch for this canvas (Coll. W. P. Chrysler, Jr.) is reproduced in Barr, p.117.

12 March 1932   *Plate 32*

127   The Mirror

Oil on canvas: 51¼×38¼ in. (130×97 cm.)
Dated on the stretcher: *12 mars xxxii*
z.VII.378
Lent by the Gustav Stern Foundation, Inc., U.S.A.

The device of placing a mirror in a picture so as to give an additional view of the subject occurs in another painting of the same year, *Girl Before a Mirror* (Museum of Modern Art, New York, Barr, col. front).

Boisgeloup, May 1932   *Plate 32*

128   Girl with Head on Table

Oil on canvas: 16×16 in. (40·6×40·6 cm.)
Inscribed bottom left: *Picasso/Boisgeloup mai xxxii*; dated on the stretcher: *22 mai xxxii*
Lent by Mrs L. K. Elmhirst, Dartington, S. Devon

Boisgeloup, 27 July 1932   *Plate 32h*

129 Woman in a Red Armchair

Oil on canvas: $51\frac{1}{8}\times38\frac{1}{4}$ in. (130×97 cm.)
Inscribed top left: *Picasso/xxxii*; inscribed on the stretcher; *Boisgeloup 27 juillet xxxii*
z.VII.395
Lent by the Tate Gallery, London

In the spring of 1932 the existence of a new model became apparent in a long series of paintings produced with dynamic energy. The same features can be seen also in the large female heads which Picasso began to model in plaster in his studio at his newly-acquired Château de Boisgeloup. The model was a young girl, Marie-Thérèse Walter. During the next few years she was to inspire many of the paintings of sleeping or seated nudes, in which a voluptuous lunar quality is always to be found.

1932   *Plate 30b*

130 Women and Children on the Beach

Oil on canvas: $31\frac{7}{8}\times39\frac{3}{8}$ in. (81×100 cm.)
Signed bottom left (since 1955): *Picasso*
z.VIII.63
Lent by Mr Michael Hertz, Bremen

Painted after a visit to Juan-les-Pins, this picture is an elaboration of the Dinard beach scenes. The movement of the diver on the left is skilfully carried across the composition in a downward motion through the body of the girl below and up again by way of the child to the kite, near the top on the left, which she holds by a string.

Boisgeloup, 30 August 1932   *Plate 32e*

131 Bathers Playing with a Ball

Oil on canvas: $57\frac{1}{2}\times45$ in. ($146\times114\cdot5$ cm.)
Signed bottom left: *Picasso*
z.VIII.147
Lent by Mr and Mrs Victor W. Ganz, New York

This painting, when contrasted with *Women and Children on the Beach* (cat. no.130) shows Picasso's rapidly alternating concern with flat treatment of form and sculptural modelling.

6 July 1933   *Plate 32i*

132 Silenus and Companions Dancing

Gouache on paper: $13\frac{5}{8}\times17\frac{3}{4}$ in. ($34\cdot5\times45$ cm.)
Inscribed bottom right: *Picasso/Cannes 6 juillet xxxiii*
Lent by M Heinz Berggruen

Classical subjects continued to absorb Picasso in engravings and drawings (see *The Sculptor's Studio* and *Minotaur* series, Geiser, pls.58–73, 80–89). They

occur also in numerous watercolour and gouache paintings but never in large-scale compositions.

Paris, 12 November 1933   *Plate 32g*

133 Minotaur and Sleeping Woman

Pastel, gouache, Indian ink and coloured crayon on paper: $13\frac{1}{2}\times20\frac{3}{4}$ in. ($34\times51\cdot5$ cm.)
Signed bottom right: *Picasso*; inscribed top left: *Paris 12 novembre xxxiii*
z.VIII.139
Lent by M Pierre Granville, Paris

The myth of the Minotaur, monster or horned god, seemed strangely appropriate to Picasso during the years when the imminence of violent catastrophes had become a haunting reality. There are numerous drawings and engravings in which this symbol of brutish untamed strength reappears in various moods, but there are no large-scale paintings. In this case a mixture of media contributes to the power with which the image is presented.

1934   *Plate 32d*

134 Head

Oil on canvas: $21\times17\frac{1}{2}$ in. ($53\cdot5\times44\cdot5$ cm.)
Signed top left: *Picasso*
z.VIII.245
Lent by Mr Edward James, London

This head belongs to the same series as the sleeping woman (*The Mirror*, cat. no.127, and *Woman in a Red Armchair*, no.129), but here there is a suggestion that there can be a poetic analogy between a landscape and the head of a sleeping girl. The same conception occurs in paintings of reclining nudes (see z.VIII.209).

1934   *Plate 32j*

135 Woman in a Red Hat

Oil on canvas: $57\frac{5}{8}\times44\frac{3}{4}$ in. ($146\cdot5\times114$ cm.)
Signed and dated bottom right: *Picasso/xxxiv*
z.VIII.241
Lent by Mr and Mrs Ralph F. Colin, New York

There are several paintings of this date of a woman gaily dressed and seated at a table.

1934   *Colour plate*

136 Girl Writing

Oil on canvas: $63\frac{7}{8}\times51\frac{3}{8}$ in. ($162\cdot5\times130\cdot5$ cm.)
Signed and dated top right: *Picasso/xxxiv*
z.VIII.246
Lent by Mr and Mrs Samuel A. Marx, Chicago

During 1934 and the early part of 1935 Picasso painted some twenty pictures of girls, bending over a table in study. In this case the quiet concentration is accentuated by a rich glow of colour from the lamplight and the dark enclosing shadows. The contrast of cool blues and pinks in the girl's face with the strong colours around it creates a mood of silent meditation which is the antithesis of the feeling in the bullfighting scenes painted during the same year (see cat. no.137).

Boisgeloup, 1934   *Plate 34b*

137   Bullfight

Oil on canvas: $38\frac{1}{4} \times 51\frac{1}{4}$ in. (97×130 cm.)
Signed bottom left: *Picasso*
Z.VIII.229
Lent by Mr and Mrs Victor W. Ganz, New York

Picasso's interest in the bullfight was renewed by two visits to Spain in 1933 and 1934. This splendid image of the dying horse overpowered by a monstrous enemy, with the surrounding crowd absorbed by the drama, is prophetic of *Guernica* which was to be painted three years later.

Paris, 21 January 1935   *Plate 3*

138   Two Women (La Muse)

Oil on canvas: 51×65 in. (130×165 cm.)
Inscribed on the stretcher: *Paris 21 janvier xxxv*
Z.VIII.256
Lent by the Musée National d'Art Moderne, Paris

There are two versions of this painting, of which th second is in the collection of Governor Nelson Rockefeller of New York, as well as numerou sketches (see C.A.10, no.7/10, 1935, pp.192, 193, 2 and 241). They belong to the series of girls readin (see cat. no.136) and possess the same atmosphere secluded concentration.

Paris, 1935   *Plate 3*

139   Woman with a Hat

Oil on canvas: $23\frac{5}{8} \times 19\frac{3}{4}$ in. (60×50 cm.)
Signed bottom left: *Picasso*
Z.VIII.247
Lent by M Georges Salles, Paris

Here Picasso has constructed a head with extraordin ary economy of means, which gives the impressio of a personality of unyielding strength and yet pre serves the fragile ornaments of female vanity.

1936 – 45   **Picasso Furioso**

Paris
Visits:
1936, 1937, 1938, Mougins (Alpes-
     Maritimes) with Dora Maar

     1936, Takes studio 7 rue des
         Grands Augustins and lives
         23 rue la Boëtie, Paris

1939, summer, Antibes
1939, September to 1940, October,
     Royan (near Bordeaux)
1940, Return to Paris

An understanding of classical mythology combined with a heredi tary passion for the bullfight had led Picasso to meditate on th strange personality of the Minotaur. In a series of etchings known *The Sculptor's Studio*, 1933, and in some remarkable drawings of th same period, this equivocal beast is seen, sometimes amorous, some times ferocious and sometimes blind, penetrating into huma society. The subconscious power of the myth and Picasso's long standing love of allegory served him as a basis for a great ne painting which he was to produce in 1937. The mural whic Picasso produced for the Spanish Pavilion in the Paris Exhibitio that year was inspired by his anger at the destruction of the Basqu capital Guernica. This great painting, now on loan to the Museu of Modern Art, New York, is a composition which expresse magnificently the anguish of a great human disaster and owes i power to Picasso's development through cubism to a new visu language.

Although *Guernica* was painted with extraordinary spee Picasso found time to preface the final picture with many studie such as the *Horse's Head*, 2 May 1937 (cat. no.143), and the *Woman Weeping*, June 1937 (cat. no.144). Its echoes continued into the autumn with paintings such as *Woman and Dead Child*, September 1937 (cat. no.145) and the *Woman Weeping*, 26 October 1937 (cat. no.146). These paintings are powerful concentrations of the emotions which pervade the great composition.

In all Picasso's work of this period there is a foreboding which sometimes rises to intensity in paintings such as *Cat Devouring a Bird*, 1939 (cat. nos.158–9), and at other times reaches a raucous note of grim humour, see *Woman with a Cat*, 1937 (cat. no.147). In the great canvas, *Night Fishing at Antibes* (Museum of Modern Art, New York, z.IX.316) the atmosphere of war which was to break out a few days later exists already in the sinister grimaces of the fishermen and the feckless grins of the girls standing beside their bicycles. The paintings that follow are deeply marked with Picasso's emotions of anguish bordering on despair, though at times his love for Dora Maar, who had shared his life since 1936, is evident in the brilliant drawings and portraits of her (cat. nos.148, 153, 164), and there are signs of a similar tenderness in portraits such as those of his daughter Maïa (cat. no. 151) and of Nusch, wife of Paul Eluard (cat. nos.149, 150).

As the war continued, and the situation around him became catastrophic, Picasso's reactions became increasingly intense.

There are pictures such as *Woman Dressing her Hair*, 1940 (cat. no.162) which seem to echo a violent resentment at the horror and stupidity of war. Apart from a few still-life paintings of great charm such as *The Soles*, 1940 (cat. no.161) and the landscape *Café at Royan*, 1940 (cat. no.163), the work of Picasso is full of angry dark thoughts. His studies of the human head go through violent distortions, sometimes combining the features of his love Dora Maar and the angular snout of his Afghan hound Kasbek, two heads in one revealing two contradictory moods.

Though materials were scarce, Picasso's wartime output was prodigious in painting and also in sculpture. It was in 1943 that he modelled, among others, a major piece, the *Man with the Sheep*, afterwards cast in bronze.

During the comfortless winter of 1941 Picasso surprised his friends by writing in four days a short drama, entitled *Desire Caught by the Tail*. In this it can be seen that his sense of the ridiculous and his understanding of the pathetic insecurity and weakness of the human condition never left him. A further example is the painting, *First Steps*, 1943 (cat. no.170). In pictures such as these Picasso illuminates with ideas of enduring importance the forbidding claustrophobic gloom of war-time surroundings: see *Still Life with Sausage* 1941 (cat. no.165). The still-life paintings are permeated with a sense of death whose emblem appears frequently in company with a shrouded lamp and withered plants; see *Still Life with a Lamp*, 1945–6 (Janis pl.63). These paintings culminated at the end of the war in another great painting, *The Charnel House* (cat. no.178), painted in the summer of 1945, which is the epitome of Picasso's feelings concerning the horror of war and its universal consequences.

Towards the end of the war, in a happier mood, Picasso painted several landscapes from the *quais* near his studio, of the city in which he had spent these years of misery with his friends.

Paris, 12 August – 2 October 1936   *Plate 31b*

140 Reclining Nude

Oil on canvas: $51\frac{1}{4} \times 63\frac{3}{4}$ in. (130 × 162 cm.)
Signed top left (since 1955): *Picasso*
Dated on the back: *12 août xxxvi – 2 octobre xxxvi*
z.VIII.310
Lent from a private collection, France

This painting shows clearly, once again, Picasso's power of using form and colour to evoke deep and elusive impressions. The naked figure of a woman lies on a bed before an open window through which the moon and the stars enter into her dreams. Grey and violet in the colouring is appropriate to the phantasmagoria of her trance, and the childlike gesture of her arms, spread wide across the pillow, unites the crowded and untidy attic with the vault of the night.

15 December 1936   *Plate 33b*

141 Still Life

Oil on canvas: $14\frac{1}{2} \times 23\frac{1}{2}$ in. (36·8 × 59·7 cm.)
Signed bottom right: *Picasso*; dated bottom left: *15 december xxxvi*.
z.VIII.311
Lent by Mrs A. T. Kessler, Preston, Rutland

Paris, 18 February 1937   *Plate 33c*

142 Seated Woman with a Book

Oil and pastel on canvas: $51\frac{1}{8} \times 38\frac{1}{8}$ in. (130 × 97 cm.)
Dated on the stretcher: *18/2/37*
z.VIII.351
Lent by the artist

Linked closely to the bone structures of 1930 and 1931 (see *Seated Bather*, cat. no.124), this painting

gives greater importance to the solidity of the body, which assumes monumental proportions when compared with the minute features of the face.

2 May 1937   *Plate 34a*

143 Horse's Head

Oil on canvas: $25\frac{1}{2} \times 36\frac{1}{4}$ in. (65 × 92 cm.)
Dated top left: *2 mai 37*
z.IX.11
Lent by the artist, through the courtesy of the Museum of Modern Art, New York

After the destruction of Guernica, the ancient capital of the Basque people in northern Spain, on 27 April, 1937, by German bombers flying for General Franco, Picasso turned the fury this action aroused in him to the creation of a great mural for the Spanish Republican pavilion at the Paris Exhibition. In June the mural was installed. Since then it has travelled widely. It was shown in London and Manchester in 1938, and in Paris and several European capitals in 1955–6. It now has a place of honour in the Museum of Modern Art, New York, as one of the greatest paintings of this century.

This study for the dying horse, which becomes a central actor in Picasso's rendering of the tragedy in his own mythological language, is an example of the depth of expression which he achieved not only in the great mural itself but in the numerous studies and postscripts (see cat. nos.144–6). Full documentation can be found in c.A, 12, nos.4/5 1937, and Juan Larrea, *Guernica*, New York, 1947.

Paris, 22 June 1937   *Plate 33f*

144 Woman Weeping

Oil on canvas: 24⅜×20 in. (62×51 cm.)
Formerly dated: *22/6/37* on the back; now relined
Z.IX.50
Lent by Mme Dora Maar, Paris

This is one of the studies for *Guernica*. Compare
Pleureuse, painted the same day (J. Larrea, *Guernica*,
New York, 1947, no.82) and two later engravings
of 2 July 1937 (*op. cit.* nos.89, 90).

Paris, 26 September 1937   *Plate 35b*

145 Woman and Dead Child

Oil on canvas: 51¼×76¾ in. (30·2×95 cm.)
Dated on the stretcher: *26 septembre 37*
Z.IX.69
*Lent by the artist, through the courtesy of the Museum of
Modern Art, New York*

On his return to Paris from Mougins at the end of
the summer of 1937 Picasso again took up the theme
of *Guernica* in 'postscripts' to the great mural. The
figure of the woman is a variation of the figure on
the right in the mural, while the child recalls the
dead baby in the arms of the woman on the extreme
left. It is in the head of the woman that Picasso has
concentrated the most violent pitch of emotion.

Paris, 26 October 1937   *Plate 35a*

146 Woman Weeping

Oil on canvas: 23½×19¼ in. (60×49 cm.)
Signed and dated right: *Picasso/37*; dated on the
stretcher: *26 octobre 37*
Z.IX.73
Lent from a private collection, London

Picasso did not altogether abandon the agonizing
theme of *Guernica* until late in the autumn of 1937.
The majority of the preliminary studies had been
painted in subdued, acid hues, or entirely in monochrome, like the great mural itself. But in this
case an explosion of strident colour is used to enhance the despairing misery and terror expressed in
the woman's face. The agony becomes all the more
intense in contrast with the frivolous costume, in
which she seems to have been unexpectedly caught.
Cubist devices such as the two eyes on the same profile, the transparency of the handkerchief and the
hands pressed to the face, used with consummate
skill, help to intensify the emotional effect.

Mougins, 30 August 1937   *Plate 33e*

147 Woman with a Cat

Oil on canvas: 31⅞×25½ in. (81×65 cm.)
Signed and dated left: *Picasso/37*; dated on the
stretcher: *30 août 1937*
Z.VIII.373
Lent by Dr Henri Laugier, Paris

After the immense effort which went into the painting of the great monochrome canvas of *Guernica* in
the summer of 1937, Picasso visited Mougins where,
in the company of his new companion, Dora Maar,
the poet Paul Eluard and other friends, he painted
landscapes, again flooded with colour, and vented
his exuberant energy on portraits which were often
grotesque and playful, and were brilliant comments
on his friends. This 'portrait' of a woman suckling
a kitten originated as a ribald caricature of Paul
Eluard.

1937   *Plate 33d*

148 Portrait of D. M.

Oil on canvas: 36¼×25½ in. (92×65 cm.)
Dated on the stretcher: *1937*
Z.VIII.331
Lent by the artist

The device of placing the two eyes on the same side
of a face seen in profile can be traced back to inventive reconstructions of the human head as early as
1927, in which full face and profile are merged
together (see Z.VII.67 and 68); but it is also a logical
development from the cubist conceptual necessity
of painting what is known to exist. In this splendid
portrait of Dora Maar this device, far from being a
mannerism or a monstrous invention, gives a sense
of tender envelopment, a fulness to the head and a
vitality to the expression which promotes it to a
work of genius.

Paris, 1937   *Plate 33i*

149 Portrait of Nusch

Oil on canvas: 36¼×25⅝ in. (92×65 cm.)
Unsigned
Z.VIII.377
Lent by the artist

The lyrical tenderness with which Picasso can
express himself is here well illustrated in this portrait
of Paul Eluard's wife, rapidly painted after a visit
they had paid him one morning in his studio.

150 Portrait of Nusch

Oil on canvas: $21\frac{5}{8} \times 18\frac{1}{8}$ in. $(55 \times 46$ cm.)
Signed and dated bottom left: *Picasso 37*
Lent by M Heinz Berggruen

Nusch, the wife of the poet Paul Eluard, inspired many paintings by Picasso between 1936 and the outbreak of war. Her fragile beauty (see cat. no.149) sometimes evoked great tenderness in treatment and at other times became elaborated into a high-spirited fantasy in which, however, her features and her vivacity were always apparent.

Paris, 16 January 1938 *Plate 33g*

151 Maïa with a Sailor Doll

Oil on canvas: $28\frac{3}{4} \times 23\frac{5}{8}$ in. $(73 \times 60$ cm.)
Dated bottom left: *16.1.38*
Z.IX.99
Lent by the artist

There are at least two other portraits of Maïa, the artist's daughter, painted during the same period (Barr, p.212; Milan, pl.81). Again the two eyes are situated in the same profile in a way that gives movement to the expression. The device is used in a spirit of tenderness rather than caricature (see *Portrait of D. M.*, cat. no.148).

Paris, 29 March 1938 *Plate 33h*

152 Cock

Pastel on paper: $30\frac{1}{2} \times 21\frac{1}{4}$ in. $(77 \cdot 5 \times 54$ cm.)
Signed and dated bottom right: *Picasso/29.3.38*
Z.IX.113
Lent by Mr and Mrs Ralph F. Colin, New York

In the mythology recreated by Picasso, birds and animals present their own legendary attributes. The cock, well armed with ferocious beak and spurs and the arrogance of his plumage, is one of the characters which reappear on Picasso's 'stage', both in painting and in sculpture.

24 May 1938 *Plate 42a*

153 Portrait of D. M.

Oil on canvas: $28\frac{1}{2} \times 24\frac{1}{2}$ in. $(72 \cdot 3 \times 62 \cdot 2$ cm.)
Signed and dated bottom left: *Picasso/38*
Z.IX.157
Lent by Mr Walter P. Chrysler, Jr, New York

A magnificent example of Picasso's ability to simplify and distort yet still retain the essential quality of a portrait – a penetrating likeness.

2 July 1938 *Plate 42b*

154 Head of a Girl with Poem

Oil on canvas: $25\frac{5}{8} \times 19\frac{5}{8}$ in. $(65 \times 50$ cm.)
Inscribed left: *2 / juillet / 38 / goute* A */ goute /* VIVACE */* MEURT LE */* BLEU PALE */* ENTRE LES */* GRIFFES DU */* VERT AMANDE */* A L'ECHELLE */* DU ROSE */ Picasso*
Z.IX.170
Lent from a private collection

In his desire to use techniques and materials in unconventional ways, to penetrate the barriers between the arts, Picasso inscribed poems on his drawings or canvases. This happened particularly during the 'thirties when he wrote several poems rich in imagery, and spent much of his time with Paul Eluard and other surrealist poets.

Paris, 19 November 1938 *Plate 36a*

155 Still Life with Black Bull's Head

Oil on canvas: $38\frac{1}{4} \times 51\frac{1}{4}$ in. $(97 \times 130$ cm.)
Signed top right: *Picasso*
Z.IX.240
Lent by Colonel Valdemar Ebbesen, Copenhagen

This painting was followed by a second version of the same subject, dated one week later. Both are dominated by the naked flame of the candle and the head of the bull, but in the second version (Coll. Ambassador and Mrs William A. M. Burden, New York, Z.IX.239), the bull's head has been flayed and its raw flesh and staring eyes give an acute sensation of physical pain. Sabartès who was Picasso's daily companion at the time, gives an intimate account of a painful attack of sciatica through which Picasso was living at the time he was painting this picture.

8 December 1936 *Plate 26d*

156 Still Life with Fish

Oil on canvas: $19\frac{3}{4} \times 24$ in. $(50 \times 61$ cm.)
Signed and dated bottom right: *Picasso/8D/36*; dated on the stretcher: *8D xxxvi*
Lent by the McRoberts and Tunnard Gallery, London

21 January 1939 *Plate 42f*

157 Woman Lying on a Couch

Oil on canvas: $38\frac{1}{4} \times 51$ in. $(97 \times 130$ cm.)
Signed and dated right: *21/1/39 Picasso*
Z.IX.252
Lent by Mr and Mrs Victor W. Ganz, New York

Probably the most disturbing feature of this uncouth odalisque is the enormous size of the head crowned with its triple coiffure. The disproportion becomes all the more surprising in its proximity with other objects, such as the trees seen through the window and the palette hanging on the wall, which have not suffered the same distortion. The audacious formation o the head looking in both directions contains, however – and perhaps on this account – both a dignity and a sensuality in keeping with the ambiguity of its regard.

Le Tremblay-sur-Mauldre, April 1939   *Plate 37a*

58 Cat Eating a Bird

Oil on canvas: 38× 50¾ in. (97× 129 cm.)
Signed bottom right: *Picasso*
z.IX.297
Lent from a private collection

With the increasing sense of impending disasters, the subjects of Picasso's work tended to be those that could allow him expression of these feelings. The mythical relations of animals and men provided him with motives for many paintings, including *Guernica*. The sense of callous cruelty emerges with great power from paintings such as this, the *Girl with a Cock* (Coll. Mrs Meric Callery, New York, z.IX.109), and the *Cock* (cat. no.152). Picasso painted two versions of this subject in April 1939 (see cat. no.159) and a third in 1953 (Coll. Rosengart, Lucerne).

Le Tremblay-sur-Mauldre, 22 April 1939   *Plate 42g*

59 Cat Eating a Bird

Oil on canvas: 32× 39⅜ in. (81× 100 cm.)
Dated top left: *22.4.39*; dated on the stretcher: *22.4.39*
z.IX.296
Lent by the artist
See note to cat. no.158

31 October 1939   *Plate 42c*

60 The Yellow Sweater

Oil on canvas: 31⅞× 25⅝ in. (81× 65 cm.)
Signed and dated top left: *Picasso/31.10.39* dated on the back: *31.10.39*
Lent by M Heinz Berggruen

This is an example of Picasso's masterly ability to create contrasts in texture with great economy of means.

Royan, 29 March 1940   *Plate 37b*

161 Soles

Oil on canvas: 23⅝× 36¼ in. (60×92 cm.)
Signed and dated bottom left: *29.3.40 Picasso*; dated on the stretcher: *29/3/40*
z.x.375
Lent by Le Marquis de Pomereu, Paris

On the 27, 28 and 29 March 1940 (see z.x.375, 376, 377) Picasso painted three versions of still lifes with fish. This is the ultimate version and the most completely resolved. Rhythms and transparencies envelope the scales and the fish, giving the subtle effect of shifting submarine light.

Royan, 1940   *Plate 38a*

162 Woman Dressing her Hair

Oil on canvas: 51¼× 38⅛ in. (130×97 cm.)
Signed top right: *Picasso*; dated on the stretcher: *6 mars 1940*
z.x.302
Lent by Mrs Louise R. Smith, New York

Despite the date on the stretcher, this picture may have been painted early in June 1940. It seems probable from the evidence of drawings made on 4 and 8 June (see z.x.535–40) that it reflects Picasso's dismay and anger at the arrival of German troops on the Atlantic coast where he was staying. The extraordinary power in the anatomical inventions and their monumental solidity is increased by the restrained but sinister colouring. The narrow insolent look in the eyes, the distended belly, the aggressive swing of the breasts suggesting the form of a swastika and the horror of the squat legs finishing in enormous ill-formed feet makes this terrifying female a most disquieting image associated with catastrophic events.

Royan, 15 August 1940   *Plate 42i*

163 Café at Royan

Oil and ripolin on canvas: 38¼× 51¼ in. (97× 130 cm.)
Inscribed on the back and on the stretcher: *Royan 15/8/40*
Lent by the artist

This delightful landscape of the quay at Royan seen from 'Les Voiliers', a villa of which Picasso had rented the top floor, was painted a few days before he returned to Paris for the rest of the war. There is a drawing of this subject (see z.x.548).

Paris, 1941 *Plate 42e*

164 Portrait of D.M.

Oil on canvas: 21⅝ × 18⅛ in. (55 × 46 cm.)
Signed and dated top left: *Picasso/41*; dated on the
stretcher: *29 mai 41*
JANIS, pl.49
Lent from the Estorick Collection, London

Picasso continued throughout these years to make
many portraits of Dora Maar, some of which, like
this, are admirable likenesses, while others go through
various degrees of distortion and dislocation of the
features until they lose any immediate resemblance to
the original model (see *Head of a Woman*, cat. no.173).

Paris, 10 May 1941 *Plate 43a*

165 Still Life with Sausage

Oil on canvas: 35 × 25½ in. (89 × 64·8 cm.)
Signed bottom left centre: *Picasso*
JANIS, pl.60
Lent by Mr and Mrs Victor W. Ganz, New York

Picasso is always alive to the objects and the atmosphere of his surroundings. Here he has represented –
not without a certain grim humour – the sordid
misery of dimmed lights and the humble wartime
meal in which a blood sausage is a rare and honoured
dish, and the gleaming knives and hungry forks made
ready for the attack.

Paris, winter 1941–2 *Plate 42h*

166 Woman Seated in a Chair

Oil on canvas: 51¼ × 38⅛ in. (130 × 97 cm.)
Signed left: *Picasso*
Lent by M Heinz Berggruen

During the war years Picasso painted a large number
of half-length pictures of seated women. This subject occurs throughout his work, but there are certain characteristics in this series that are not found
either in the portraits of the early years or in the
more impersonal aesthetic inventions of cubism. The
most important is a disquieting emotional quality
which arises not only from the violence and origin-
ality of the distortions but also from the apparent
contrast between the head, which is submitted to
startling and inventive rearrangements, and the body,
which is more readily admissible in form. The picture in question is one of the most powerful examples
of this opposition. The astonishing new organism
which grows from the woman's body, occupying
the position and displaying the easily recognizable
features of the human head, is a significant product
of familiar feelings such as love, fear and sensuality,

re-formed in a way that affects the subconscious an[d]
induces an avowal of its underlying truth. Fe[w]
artists have dared to look at woman with an eye s[o]
critical and yet so appreciative as Picasso.

Paris, 5 April 1942 *Plate 39*

167 Still Life with the Skull of a Bull

Oil on canvas: 57⅛ × 38¼ in. (130 × 97 cm.)
Signed bottom right: *Picasso*; and dated on the back[:]
5 avril 42
JANIS, pl.101
Lent by M André Lefèvre, Paris

Of the many wartime still lifes this is perhaps th[e]
most significant and powerful. The lighting concen[-]
trated on the skull set against the darkness outside [is]
full of drama, as is the void within the skull itsel[f.]
There is an earlier variant of this composition date[d]
32/4/39 (Coll. the Artist, z.IX.296), and a drawin[g]
made the same day (C. Zervos, *Dessins de Picasso*[,]
Paris, 1949, pl.114).

Paris, 1942 *Plate 40*

168 Girl with an Artichoke

Oil on canvas: 76¾ × 52 in. (195 × 132 cm.)
Signed bottom right: *Picasso*
JANIS pl.77
Lent by Mr Walter P. Chrysler, Jr, New York

Steeped in the atmosphere of Paris during the wa[r]
this sombre picture of a girl seated in a wicke[r]
chair holding the stem of an artichoke is endowe[d]
with a feeling of gravity, monumental, endurin[g]
and expectant. The drab colour recalls daily pre[-]
occupations such as the visit to the market stall an[d]
neighbourly gossip, but the transposition into th[e]
heroic which is achieved can only be accounted fo[r]
by the overwhelming proportion of the head an[d]
the expectation and wonder that appear in the eyes[.]

Paris, 30 September 1942 *Plate 43*

169 Reclining Nude

Oil on canvas: 51¼ × 76¾ in. (130 × 95 cm.)
Signed bottom left: *Picasso*; dated on the stretcher[:]
30 septembre 42
JANIS, pl.12
Lent by Mr and Mrs Victor W. Ganz, New York

This painting is a convincing example of the contin[-]
uity that exists in the work of Picasso, despite hi[s]
flow of revolutionary inventions. Although clues t[o]
the subject-matter are more recognizable than in th[e]
early days, the principle of a thorough analysis o[f]
form, undisturbed by the introduction of colour

and the conceptual view of the subject seen from front and back, remain essential features of the style. The ambiguous spreading of the form of the reclining figure brings with it the suggestion that it is in reality two figures combined in one.

Paris, 21 May 1943   *Plate 39a*

170   First Steps

Oil on canvas: $51\frac{1}{4} \times 38\frac{1}{4}$ in. (130×97 cm.)
Signed top left: *Picasso*
JANIS, pl.105
Lent by the Yale University Art Gallery (Gift of Stephen C. Clark)

Throughout the anxieties and privations of the war, Picasso worked with tremendous energy, as though in vengeance against the madness of such misfortunes. His life was dominated by the anxieties of his friends but, as can be seen in this painting, his interest and his misgivings about the future could be tempered with an irrepressible sense of humour (compare *Woman and Rocking Chair*, cat. no.172). In this painting distortion is used to enhance both the meaning of the figures and their movement. The human, as well as the formal relationship between mother and child is remarkable and has some of the spontaneous innocence and monumental intensity of a Romanesque mural.

Paris, 25 June 1943   *Plate 40b*

171   Le Vert Galant

Oil on canvas: $25\frac{5}{8} \times 36$ in. (65×92 cm.)
Dated on the back: *25 juin 43*
JANIS, pl.59
Lent by the artist

As has happened periodically throughout his life, Picasso was seized at the end of the war with a desire to paint landscapes of his immediate surroundings. He made several views of Notre Dame and the bridges and *quais* of the Ile de la Cité near his studio in the Rue des Grands Augustins. This picture shows the trees in the garden at the point of the island and the equestrian statue of Henri IV, for whom the name '*Vert Galant*' is a popular nickname.

Paris, 9 August 1943   *Plate 43c*

172   Woman and Rocking Chair

Oil on canvas: $63\frac{3}{4} \times 51\frac{1}{4}$ in. (162×130 cm.)
Dated on the stretcher: *9 août 43*
JANIS, pl.67
Lent by the Musée National d'Art Moderne, Paris

There is a taunting gaiety in this picture arising from its colour and the movement of the rocking chair,

which was a familiar piece of furniture in the artist's studio.

Paris, 1943   *Plate 38b*

173   Head of a Woman

Oil on canvas: $36\frac{1}{4} \times 28\frac{3}{4}$ in. (92×73 cm.)
Signed top left: *Picasso*; dated on the stretcher: *3 juin 43*
Lent from a private collection, France

In his analysis of the human head Picasso has often been tempted to split its unity. In many cases two faces closely interlinked can be found in the same head (see Z.VII.40 and 41) or, as in this case, the head is divided into two separate but complementary parts. The awesome austerity of this painting, in its lack of colour and precision of form, is like a monument to the tragedy of war.

Paris, 1943   *Plate 43d*

174   Woman in Green

Oil on canvas: 51×38 in. (29.5×96.5 cm.)
Signed top left: *Picasso*
Lent by Mr and Mrs James Johnson Sweeney, New York

This powerful seated figure is a splendid example of Picasso's ability to transpose a linear arabesque into three-dimensional form. The spiral, which here forms one of the breasts, is, according to Picasso, the first shape that he drew as a child because, he says, it was like a kind of sugar cake called '*torruella*' of which he was particularly fond.

Paris, 1943   *Plate 43g*

175   Head of a Youth

Gouache on paper: $12\frac{3}{4} \times 10$ in. (32.5×25.5 cm.)
Signed and dated: *Picasso 29/11/43*
JANIS, pl.134
Lent by Dr Henry M. Roland, London

On the same day Picasso painted this study for the sculpture *The Man with a Sheep* with classical tranquillity, and on the reverse side drew with flowing curves the tousled head of a bearded man with a ferocious gleam in his eyes (see Janis, pl.135).

Paris, 4 April 1944   *Plate 43e*

176   Still Life with Candle

Oil on canvas: $23\frac{5}{8} \times 36\frac{1}{4}$ in. (60×92 cm.)
Signed top right: *Picasso;* dated on the back: *4 avril (?) 44*
Lent by Mr Jacques Sarlie, New York

Although the influences of cubism are still present in this painting, there is nothing cryptic about the presentation of the subject. Just as transparency can be used to weld objects together and prevent the one hiding the other, so in this case shadow is used to enclose and fortify their presence. Compare other versions of this composition (see Janis, pls.33, 35, 36).

Paris, 4 May 1944   *Plate 43f*
177   Head
Oil on canvas: $13\frac{7}{8} \times 8\frac{3}{4}$ in. (35·2 × 22·2 cm.)
Signed top left: *Picasso;* dated on the back: *4 mai 44 IV*
Lent from a private collection

Paris, 1945   *Plate 41*
178   The Charnel House
Oil on canvas: $78\frac{5}{8} \times 98\frac{1}{2}$ in. (200 × 250 cm.)
Signed and dated bottom left: *Picasso 45*
JANIS, pl.16
Lent by Mr Walter P. Chrysler, Jr, New York

Like *Guernica*, this great painting was a deliberate attempt on the part of Picasso to express his horror of war. His motive was clear: 'No', he stated, 'painting is not done to decorate apartments; it is an instrument of war . . .' against 'brutality and darkness'. Bringing all his powers into action, using the distortions which had become his well-tried vocabulary, banishing the distractions of colour, and even denying himself the symbolism of *Guernica*, he concentrated on the appalling events of our dark age. Alfred Barr says with eloquence: 'Its figures are facts – the famished, waxen cadavers of Buchenwald, Dachau, and Belsen. The fury and shrieking violence which make the agonies of *Guernica* tolerable are here reduced to silence. For the man, the woman, and the child this picture is a *pietà* without grief, an entombment without mourners, a requiem without pomp.' (Barr, p.250.) The painting, which Picasso still considers to be unfinished, was first exhibited in the *Salon d'Automne* of 1945. It is reproduced in an early state by Barr (*op. cit.*)

1946 – 54   Antibes and Vallauris

Paris, 1945
Antibes, 1946–8
Vallauris, 1948–54
Visits:
1945, late summer, Golfe Juan and Menerbes
1946, summer, Golfe Juan
    autumn, Antibes
1946 autumn, moves to Antibes
1948 moves to Vallauris
1948, Poland
1949, Italy: Rome, Florence
1950, England: London, Sheffield
1951, lives in Paris briefly at rue Gay-Lussac
1954, summer, Collioure and Perpignan

As soon as the exhilaration of liberation and the return of old friends from abroad had subsided, Picasso made his way again to the Mediterranean. In the previous months spent in Paris he had worked intensively at lithographs, many of which were scenes of bullfights and still life subjects. Soon after his arrival in the south of France he was offered the vast halls of the Palais Grimaldi in Antibes as a studio, and the subject matter of his work changed abruptly. Again legendary figures predominated in his thoughts. The idyllic charm of nymphs, fauns, centaurs and satyrs, dancing and regaling themselves in Arcadian scenes, appeared in paintings and lithographs, and among them emerged a new face, radiant as the sun and delicate as a flower, that of Françoise Gilot, who had accompanied him. The work of this period is collected together in the museum at Antibes, forming a testimony to months of newly-won tranquillity.

In 1947, the year in which Françoise gave birth to their son Claude, Picasso became attracted by the possibilities offered by the potteries of Vallauris, and a year later he moved there with his new family. This began a period of great creative production in ceramics, an art which he treated in a similar way to polychrome sculpture. At the same time he continued to paint with great vigour. Portraits of Françoise, his son Claude and his daughter Paloma, born in 1947 and 1949, are usually brilliant in colour and decorated with vigorous flourishes and arabesques. The paintings of his children at play, reading, or lying in bed asleep show tender observation of their behaviour: see *Paloma Asleep*, 1952 (cat. no.190). Unlike the paintings of the Blue period, they are devoid of all sentimentality and reveal the complex joys and passions of childhood. The Mediterranean landscape around him was also an enchantment to Picasso both by night and by day (see *Chimneys of Vallauris*, 1951, cat. no.185, and *Moonlight at Vallauris*, 1951, cat. no.188), and remained always closely associated with his proverbial love of the sea.

The presence of Picasso brought new prosperity to Vallauris and was greatly appreciated by the inhabitants. The life-size bronze *Man with the Sheep* was set up in the main square, and Picasso was invited to decorate a small and beautiful medieval chapel which had fallen into disuse. To cover the vault of its nave, he painted in 1952 two large panels displaying allegories of war on one side and of peace on the other.

There is an abundance of variety in the styles used by Picasso during these years, varying from the almost abstract composition of the *Kitchen*, 1948 (cat. no.181) to the fantasy and playfulness of the *Sport of Pages*, 1951 (cat. no.187), This latter corresponds more closely in style to the great paintings of *War* and *Peace*, although in these the symbolic figures are treated with less detail and the overall appearance is one of grave simplicity.

Paris, 5 May 1946   *Plate 46a*

179   Girl-Flower (Portrait of Françoise Gilot)

Oil on canvas: $57\frac{1}{2} \times 35$ in. (146×89 cm.)
Dated on the back: *5 mai 1946*
JANIS, pl.122
Lent by Mme Françoise Gilot, Paris

Picasso made many portraits of Françoise Gilot. There is in particular a series of 11 lithographs (14 and 15 June 1946) drawn in quick succession. The interpretation of the face as a flower or as the sun occurs frequently.

21 March 1947   *Plate 43h*

180   Cock and Knife

Oil on canvas: $31\frac{7}{8} \times 39\frac{3}{8}$ in. (81×100 cm.)
Signed top left: *Picasso*; dated on the back: *21/3/47*
Lent by Mr and Mrs Victor W. Ganz, New York

The formal and symbolic qualities of this painting make it exceptional among still lifes in which food,

fruit and wine are part of the composition. In this case the theme is a trussed cock lying beside the knife that has cut its throat. A dead bird appears as the principal element in a series of still lifes of 1919 (see z.III.283–5); it occurs also in a composition of 1921 (z.VI.335) and again in 1942, but here it is the lonely presence of the slaughtered bird which is all important. (For a first version of this painting, less free in style, see c.A. 24 1949, p.246.)

Paris, 9 November 1948   *Plate 44b*

181   The Kitchen

Oil on canvas: $68\frac{7}{8} \times 98\frac{3}{8}$ in. (175×250 cm.)
Dated on the back
Lent by the artist

On several occasions since he took the conclusive step away from conventional representation in *Les Demoiselles d'Avignon*, Picasso has sacrificed the recognizable image for a more or less complete form of abstraction. An early example is the collage *Head* of c.1913 (see cat. no.68), and another is a series of drawings made at Juan-les-Pins in 1924 which were later incorporated in the illustrations for Balzac's *Le Chef d'Œuvre Inconnu*, published by Vollard in 1931 (see z.v.276-9 etc.) This great canvas, based on the utensils and furniture of his kitchen in Paris, resembles the rhythms of the drawings of 1924. It is an abstraction in the form of a great arabesque in which lines, circles, arrows, and nodes are built up into a pattern which becomes again organic and vital, passing through abstraction to a new sense of activity. It can be enjoyed for its purely non-figurative qualities as a composition, or as a lively assembly of the pots, pans and birdcages that festoon the kitchen wall. There is another version, painted at the same time, which closely resembles this in size and composition. In this, certain details such as birds and patterned plates forming nodal points are clearly recognizable (see Milan, no.125).

21 March 1949   *Plate 46c*

182   Portrait of Françoise

Oil on canvas: 24×15 in. (61×38 cm.)
Signed top left: *Picasso;* dated on the back: *21/3/49II*
Lent by M Heinz Berggruen

Vallauris, 20 January 1950   *Plate 46b*

183   Claude and Paloma

Ripolin and oil on wood: 51¼×38¼ in.
(116×89 cm.)
Inscribed on the back: *vendredi 20/1/50 Vallauris*
Lent by the artist

The ability to incorporate various styles in the same picture has already been apparent, though to a less striking degree, even in the cubist period (see *Still life with Chair Caning*, cat. no.61, and *Playing card, Fruit dish, Glass*, cat. no.77), but here the contrast between the treatment of the face of the artist's daughter Paloma and that of his son Claude is very noticeable. The strong overall pattern of the painting envelopes the figures of the two children and unites them with the design of the floor – a faithful transcription of the tiles paving their home in Vallauris. As a result, features in themselves incongruous are firmly welded into the composition.

Vallauris, 22 February 1950   *Plate 44a*

184   Portrait of a Painter, after El Greco

Oil on wood: 40×32¼ in. (100·5×81 cm.)
Signed bottom left: *Picasso*; inscribed on the back:
Vallauris 22/2/50
Lent by Mlle Angela Rosengart, Lucerne

The interpretation of a work of art is often as interesting and as valid as the study of natural objects.

Picasso has frequently taken the work of another painter as his starting-point and has developed it with great freedom according to his own inspiration. The *Portrait of a Painter* – possibly his son – painted by El Greco between 1594 and 1604, now in the museum at Seville, is the origin of this painting in which Picasso has wittily transposed the style of the 16th-century master into his own idiom.

Vallauris, 12 January 1951   *Plate 46d*

185   Chimneys of Vallauris

Oil on canvas: 23⅝×28¾ in. (60×73 cm.)
Dated on the back: *12/1/51*
Lent by the artist

Again in Vallauris Picasso painted landscapes of his immediate surroundings by day or by night and in all seasons. The black smoke rising from the kilns in the little town where he also worked on his ceramics was a normal feature in the landscape.

Vallauris, 25 January 1951   *Plate 46e*

186   Mother and Children with an Orange

Oil on wood: 45¼×34¾ in. (115×88 cm.)
Inscribed on the back: *25/1/51*
Lent by the artist

The theme of motherhood, which has periodically occupied a place of importance in Picasso's work, reappears during the childhood of Claude and Paloma. Compare *Mother and Child on a White Background* (Milan, no.177).

Vallauris, 24 February 1951   *Plate 46f*

187   The Knight (Sport of Pages)

Oil on wood: 21¼×25½ in. (56·5×64·8 cm.)
Dated on the back: *24/2/51*
Lent by the artist

Picasso's preoccupation with the menace of war was expressed once more in a large composition, *Massacre in Korea* (Coll. the artist), painted in January 1951, and again in the great murals *War* and *Peace* painted for the Romanesque vault of a chapel in Vallauris. At the same time Picasso made several drawings and lithographs in the style of a light-hearted medieval allegory. The charger overladen with trappings is related to its more tragic brothers, the funeral horses of the panel representing *War*.

Vallauris, 1951 *Plate 46h*

188 Moonlight at Vallauris

Oil on wood: 54× 41 in. (137× 104 cm.)
Signed top left: *Picasso*
Lent by the Galerie de l'Europe, Paris

Picasso painted many landscapes of the houses and terraced gardens that he saw from his villa at Vallauris. Of these surroundings in which the summer night has charms which rival the light of day, Paul Eluard wrote: 'He copies the night as he would copy an apple, from memory, the night in his garden at Vallauris – a sloping garden, ordinary enough. . . . I realize from the start that these nights at Vallauris will have nothing of the facile grace of Provence, but I am certain that after seeing them I could never live through another Provençal night without feeling it in the way it exists in his pictures. All Picasso's models resemble their portraits.' There is another night landscape painted in the same year, similar in intensity and in composition (Coll. Richard K. Weil, St. Louis, see Milan, no.152).

Paris, 16 April 1952 *Plate 45a*

189 Skull of a Goat, Bottle and Candle

Oil on canvas: 35× 45⅝ in. (89× 116 cm.)
Signed bottom right: *Picasso*; dated on the back: *16/4/52*
Lent by the Tate Gallery, London

The head or the skull of a goat occupies an important place in the paintings and drawings after 1950 and there also exists a fine bronze sculpture of a goat which dates from the same year. A large panel of a goat was painted in 1950 (Milan, no.149) and there are two other versions of this picture (Milan, nos. 164, 166), as well as a painted bronze (Coll. the Museum of Modern Art, New York). The skull alone is found in two aquatints (1952 and 1953). The overall linear pattern of this composition and the lack of colour relate it to a much larger painting of 1948, *The Kitchen* (cat. no.181).

Vallauris, 28 December 1952 *Plate 46g*

190 Paloma Asleep

Oil on wood: 44⅞× 57½ in. (114× 146 cm.)
Signed top left: *Picasso*
Lent by Mrs Louise R. Smith, New York

Picasso's observation of children has always been acute. In this case the attitude of the child in the abandonment of sleep is rendered with tenderness and at the same time with a powerful sculptural realization of its form.

Vallauris, 1953 *Plate 46i*

191 Girl Reading with Red Background

Ripolin on wood: 31⅞× 39⅜ in. (81× 100 cm.)
Signed top right: *Picasso*
Lent by Mrs Leon Bagrit, London

There are four other paintings of Françoise absorbed in reading a book, dated 1953 (see Milan, nos.175, 178, 179, 180). In this version the treatment of the head is of exceptional interest. The ambiguity in its form allows one to consider it as two heads, though by elision they are also welded into one. Françoise reading is closely watched over by the figure of her son Claude. There is an expression of warm affection in the way in which even the mouths are united.

Paris, Vallauris, 7 March 1954 *Plate 47c*

192 The Coiffure

Oil on canvas: 51⅝× 38¼ in. (130·5× 97 cm.)
Signed top right: *Picasso*; dated on the back: *7.3.54*
Lent by M Siegfried Rosengart, Lucerne

There is in this picture again a contradiction in style between the figure of the boy, which evokes the youths of the Saltimbanque period (1906), and the figure of the nude woman, which bears witness to cubist technique; but once more this contrast in no way interferes with the unity of the composition.

18 March 1954 *Plate 47a*

193 Seated Nude

Oil on canvas: 51¼× 38¼ in. (130× 97 cm.)
Signed and dated top left: *Picasso 18.3.54*; dated on the back: *18.3.54*
Lent by M Siegfried Rosengart, Lucerne

Cubist technique is again responsible for the completeness of vision presented in this picture. The back and front views of the figure are combined with astonishing ease, and the contrast between the figure and its evenly-coloured background gives a richness to the composition.

Vallauris, 2 June 1954 *Plate 47b*

194 Portrait of J. R. with Roses

Oil on canvas: 39⅜× 31⅞ in. (100× 81 cm.)
Dated on the back: *2 juin 1954*
Lent by the artist

This is one of the first portraits of Jacqueline Roque. This eloquent expression of female charm and dignity is a symbol of Picasso's affection for his companion of recent years. The firm stylized drawing of the figure is brilliantly contrasted with the freer and more literal treatment of the flowers in the background.

On 13 December 1954 Picasso began work on a series of fifteen variations on Delacroix's painting *The Women of Algiers* (cat. no 196), which he finished on 15 February 1955. This was not the first time that he had taken the theme of a painting which he admired and without any intention of copying the original, used it as a basis for variations on the composition in his own terms. Previous examples came from very varied sources: Le Nain in 1917 (z.iii.96) Renoir in 1919 (z.iii.428–30), Poussin in 1944 (Barr, p.243) Cranach in 1947–9 (Mourlot, *Picasso Lithographe*, Paris, vol.ii, 1950 109 and 109 bis), Courbet and El Greco in 1950 (Verve, vol.vii Paris, 1951, nos.25, 26) and more recently Velázquez, *Las Meninas* (The Ladies in Waiting) (cat. nos.202–59). There are two versions of the Delacroix *Les Femmes d'Alger*: one in the Louvre and the other in the Musée Fabre at Montpellier, but Picasso states that he had not seen either of them for many years. His visual memory allowed him, however, to work on the variations even without the aid of a reproduction. In quick succession he painted a number of variations, some in monochrome and others with brilliant colour interpreting the composition and the anatomy of the women with his usual boldness. The same trend, beginning with more representational studies and arriving at nearly abstract conceptions in the latest work, can be found in the series of *Las Meninas*, painted three years later.

After his rupture with Françoise Gilot in 1953 Picasso found a new and devoted companion in Jacqueline Roque. His love for her is evident in portraits painted in June 1954; see *J. R. with Roses* (cat. no.194). With her he installed himself in the villa *La Californie*, overlooking the sea near Cannes. Although the architecture of this house is in no way pleasing it afforded him ample space for his work and its interior, often with Jacqueline seated among his canvases and sculpture, became the theme for many important paintings. The diversity of his activities, with ample working space at Cannes and Vallauris still within reach, became even greater; painting, sculpture, ceramics, engraving and lithography occupied the greater part of his time. In addition, in the summer of 1953 he became the sole star performer in a film produced by Georges Clouzot entitled *Le Mystère Picasso*.

The paintings of recent years combine the many experiences through which he has lived. The influence of cubism is always apparent and his mastery of the many styles at his disposal enables him to work with great assurance, freedom and speed. His painting is more than ever linked with sculpture. His bronzes often originate in objects that he finds and re-interprets by sticking them together in the same playful way in which he used scraps of paper and other objects in his cubist *collage*. Finally he often paints them. Intuitively he invents unconventional techniques to produce the effect he desires, and seizes on whatever means may come to hand, such as the feathers of his pigeons picked up from the floor instead of a brush: see *L'Arlésienne*, 1958 (cat. no.262).

In the autumn of 1958 Picasso embarked on a concentrated period of work during which he shut himself off from his friends for more than two months. During this time he painted a series of variations on *Las Meninas* of Velázquez. The original had been known and admired by Picasso ever since he visited Madrid with his father at the age of 14. With audacious emphasis he interpreted the dramatic qualities of the composition in a great variety of ways. Using the simplest means, he ingeniously transformed Velázquez's handling of the lighting, the placing of the figures, their gestures and even the texture of their dresses. During this period, concentrated on this one great theme, Picasso used as a variant to the pleasure he found in painting the landscape and the doves which nested on the balcony from his studio window. These pictures, full of the clarity of Mediterranean sunlight, form a delightful contrast to the sombre interior of the Spanish court.

Other major works have occupied Picasso in recent years, in particular the great mural which he painted for the UNESCO building in Paris. The astonishing way in which this gigantic painting fits into its surroundings without Picasso's having been able to see it in place is once more evidence of his understanding of visual problems. Again the subject has allegorical overtones, but, as in all great art, its interpretation must remain ambiguous. The mural itself is a bold and splendid decoration.

The increased popularity of bullfighting in France in recent years, and its inevitable associations with Spain, have revived Picasso's passion for the arena. On his return from a bullfight in Arles in the autumn of 1958 he stopped at the Château de Vauvenargues, which was then for sale, and a few days later became the owner. This ancient château is situated below the slopes of the Mont Ste Victoire, made famous in the paintings of Cézanne. On various occasions in the last months he has escaped to its seclusion where he continues to paint with great energy. It is apparent in these works that he is always deeply sensitive to his surroundings. The colour and the

subjects appear to emanate from the rocks and the pine trees o
Provence that surround him. Among his latest works there are
landscapes and still-life compositions revealing an acute vision and
a youthful vigour. In addition there are portraits of Jacqueline
Roque, in brilliant colours which recall his Spanish origin.

Cannes, 11 October 1954   *Plate 49b*

195   Jacqueline with a Black Scarf

Oil on canvas: 36¼ × 28½ in. (92 × 72·5 cm.)
Inscribed top left: *Pour Jacqueline/aimée/Picasso*;dated
on the back: *11/10/54*
Lent by the artist

This is one of the many pictures painted in recent
years of Jacqueline Roque. It is an admirable and
life-like portrait.

Paris, 14 February 1955   *Plate 45b*

196   Women of Algiers (Final version)

Oil on canvas: 44⅞ × 57½ in. (114 × 146 cm.)
Dated on the back: *14/2/55*
Lent by Mr and Mrs Victor W. Ganz, New York

Between 13 December 1954 and 14 February 1955
Picasso painted a series of fifteen paintings of which
this is the last. They were all variations on the picture
by Delacroix, painted in 1834 and now in the Louvre,
entitled *The Women of Algiers*, of which there is a
second smaller version of 1849 in the Musée Fabre
at Montpellier. This exercise, from which Picasso
drew great satisfaction, produced an extraordinary
variety in the colour and composition of each canvas.
Starting with easily recognizable forms and an abundance of colour, the paintings reached in the eleventh
version a state of abstraction in monochrome, but
regained their colour and a partially representational
style in the final version. They were all painted
without any immediate reference to Delacroix's
pictures.

Cannes, 10 July 1955   *Plate 47d*

197   Seated Woman

Oil on canvas: 36¼ × 28¾ in. (92 × 73 cm.)
Signed and dated top left: *10.7.55/Picasso*; dated on
the back: *10.7.55I.*
Lent by Mlle Angela Rosengart, Lucerne

Cannes, 23 October 1955   *Plate 48*

198   The Studio

Oil on canvas: 76½ × 50¾ in. (194·8 × 129·7 cm.)
Signed top right: *Picasso*; dated on the back: *23.10.55 I*
Lent by the Galerie Rosengart, Lucerne

The early 20th century decoration of the villa *La
Californie*, with palm trees seen through the windows, provided Picasso with a theme for a long
series of paintings, big and small, of the interior of his
studio. He used the great variety of objects which
rapidly overcrowded the room, including pieces of
his own sculpture and new canvases, as features in
his compositions. The majority of these works were
exhibited in April 1957 at the Galerie Louise Leiris
in Paris (see C.A. 31, 1956–7, pp.5–78).

Cannes, February – April 1956   *Plate 48a*

199   Two Nudes

Oil on canvas: 76¾ × 51¼ in. (195 × 130 cm.)
Dated on the back: *4.1.56*
Lent by the artist

This composition with two figures is a further development of paintings such as the *Reclining Nude*, 1942
(cat. no.169) and the *Seated Woman*, 1955 (cat. no.
197). Its debt to cubism is obvious.

Cannes, 30 March 1956   *Plate 47i*

200   The Studio at Cannes

Oil on canvas: 44⅛ × 57½ in. (112 × 146 cm.)
Dated on the back: *30/3/56*
Lent by the artist

There are two main variations among the paintings
of 1955–6 of studio interiors: those with a vertical
treatment in which the tall windows and palm trees
outside dominate the composition (see cat. no.198),
and those which are horizontal, and usually showing
canvases distributed around the room. In some of
them Jacqueline Roque in profile is seated in a rocking chair. In this version, to the left, there is a
Moroccan brass coffee tray reminiscent of the
Women of Algiers and the odalisques of Matisse.

Cannes, 19 May 1956　　　　　　　　*Plate 47e*

201 Bullfight

Oil on canvas: 19⅝ × 24 in. (50 × 61 cm.)
Signed bottom: *Picasso*; dated on the back: *19.5.56*
Lent by Mr and Mrs Daniel Saidenberg, New York

With easy access to the arenas of Arles and Nîmes, Picasso has again found a constant attraction in bullfighting. Though paintings of this subject have been relatively rare, he has made many lithographs, and in 1957 he lavishly illustrated a 17th century book on *Tauromachia* by José Delgado (Pepe Illo). This painting, abounding in gaiety and charm, shows a festive aspect. It should be compared with the *corrida* seen in a tragic light (see *Bullfight*, 1934, cat. no.137).

Cannes, 17 August – 30 Dec. 1957　*Plates 49a, 50–55*

202– Las Meninas
259

58 canvases
Lent by the artist

Towards the end of the summer of 1957, Picasso moved his studio to the top floor of his villa and for the rest of the year he worked mysteriously on a series of 58 paintings, admitting a few friends only towards the end of the period. These paintings have been shown once before, in June 1959 at the Galerie Louise Leiris in Paris, where they were exhibited, as now, as a complete series.

There are two themes concurrent in these paintings; one is a series of jubilant observations of the immediate surroundings, in which the pigeons that nest on the balcony of the studio are the chief actors. Palm trees, the sea and nearby islands are their background. The other major theme consists of 44 variations on Velázquez's great picture *Las Meninas* ('The Maids in Waiting'). Picasso first saw this historic painting in Madrid at the age of 15, and he noted his first impression in a drawing which still exists, and of which a photograph is shown in this exhibition. But apart from his admiration of the picture for aesthetic and technical reasons, he had always been intrigued by the problem it poses of the relationship between the painter, the model and the spectator. Velázquez had here painted himself painting the king and queen, whose image appears in a small mirror quite insignificant in size. The picture creates a reality which is a reflection of a reflection of the model itself. This subtle introduction to the 'behind-the-scene' in the creation of a painting appealed to Picasso and he decided to explore and comment on Velázquez's conception of a problem that had haunted him for over sixty years.

In this case the first of Picasso's paintings is the largest

and the most complete of the whole series. His activity during the following month was concentrated on details; then followed further large canvases analysing and developing the composition as a whole. The last of these is dated 3 October and from then onwards he was once more occupied with groups and single figures. Finally towards the end of the series appears a portrait of the only spectator who had been allowed to witness this sustained and brilliant labour throughout – Jacqueline.

The *Meninas* series, seen individually and as a whole, gives many clues to Picasso's methods, feelings and convictions. There is a wide span between the small enchanting studies (cat. nos. 218 and 259) painted with incredible virtuosity, and the carefully constructed large canvases (cat. nos.202, 232, 234, and 235). The lighthearted ease with which many of them are painted could only have been achieved after a lifetime of dedication. Picasso has taken the work of a brother artist and submitted it to ruthless examination. He shows it no slavish respect and in his analysis it is possible at times to hear his laugh – that laughter which, to quote Baudelaire, is 'satanic, thus profoundly human and ... essentially contradictory; that is to say, it is at the same time a sign of infinite grandeur and infinite misery.' The *Meninas* series should be studied and enjoyed as a whole for its insight and its humanity. It is not only a critical study of Velázquez's style, it is also a revaluation of our conceptions of space and time in relation to our vision.

Cannes, 19 April – 9 June 1958　　　*Plate 47g*

260 The Bay at Cannes

Ripolin on canvas: 51¼ × 76¾ in. (130 × 195 cm.)
Dated on the back from 19.4.58 to 9.6.58
Lent by the artist

Space, air, a brilliant sparkle of light and the crowded buildings of the town are the constituents of this landscape. As is so often the case, Picasso has watched the scene from a height and the canvas is filled nearly to the top with sea and islands. The sky is treated as a narrow frieze (compare *Café at Royan*, 1940, cat. no.163).

Cannes, 28 May 1958　　　　　　　*Plate 47f*

261 Still Life with Bull's Skull

Ripolin on canvas: 63¾ × 51¼ in. (162 × 130 cm.)
Dated bottom left: *28.5.58*; dated on the back from 28.5.58 to 31.5.58, and 7.6.58, 9.6.58.
Lent by the artist

This vigorous composition, which should be compared to the early versions of the still life in front of a window of about 1920 (see *Table in Front of a Window*, 1919, cat. no.90 and *Window opening onto the Rue Penthièvre*, 1920, cat. no.92), was painted during a period of political crisis which worried Picasso. 'I painted it with curses', he said at the time. The movement of the clouds and the flowers, the double reflection of the sun in the window panes and the cadaverous grin of the skull are evocative of the sounding of an air-raid warning.

Cannes, July–August 1958   *Plate 47h*

262 L'Arlésienne

Ripolin on canvas: 24× 18⅛ in. (61× 46 cm.)
Dated top left from 8/7/58 to 15/8/58
Lent by the artist

The spontaneous charm of this painting remains intact in spite of the fact that Picasso worked on it almost daily for more than a month, as can be seen from the dates that decorate the left-hand margin. Once more unconventionally adopting whatever came to hand, he used the feathers of his pigeons, picked up from the floor, instead of brushes.

Vauvenargues, 18 March 1959   *Plate 47j*

263 Composition with a Dalmatian Dog

Oil on canvas: 76× 55 in. (195× 140 cm.)
Signed and dated top left: *18.3.1959 Picasso*; dated on the back: *18.3.59*
Lent by the Galerie Louise Leiris, Paris

One of the first to be made at Vauvenargues, this painting shows the influence of the austere colour of the forests below the Mont Ste. Victoire on which the Château de Vauvenargues is situated. Picasso had bought this vast rugged estate a few months before and, as is his habit, he again produced paintings which were impregnated with the colour of his new surroundings and in which the objects around him become the theme – in this case a heavily ornamented sideboard and his Dalmatian dog.

Theatre design, Decoration and Tapestries

Rome, 1917   *Plate 56a*

264 Drop Curtain for 'Parade'

Distemper on canvas: 11× 18 yards (approx.) (10× 16·40 m.)
Unsigned
z.II.**951
Lent by the Musée National d'Art Moderne, Paris

This curtain, designed by Picasso, was painted by him with the help of other artists and scene painters in Rome for the ballet *Parade*, which was first performed in Paris on 17 May 1917 at the Théâtre du

Châtelet by the Russian Ballet of Serge Diaghilev. The idea of a 'modern' ballet had originated from Cocteau, who asked Erik Satie to write the music and persuaded Picasso to design the costumes and scenery. The curtain, with its delightful composition only indirectly influenced by cubism, owes its inspiration rather to the popular art of the circus and the *commedia dell'arte*. Its purpose was to charm the audience and keep them unprepared for the shock of the ballet itself, which proved to be an outrageous attack on their conventional sensibility. Picasso's ultra-modern costumes (see z.II**952–64), the strange noises invented by Satie and the incomprehensible actions conceived by Cocteau for the dancers, set off by the able choreography of Massine, produced a startling effect, and brought a violent reaction from the audience. In the programme for *Parade*, Apollinaire announced the ballet as significant of the dawn of a new era in its creation of a super-realism (surrealism) which was to herald the New Spirit.

Paris, 1923   *Plate 56c*

265 Composition for a 'Mardi-Gras' Ball

Oil on canvas: 155× 84¼ in. (294× 214 cm.)
Signed bottom right: *Picasso*
Lent by the Chrysler Art Museum, Provincetown, Mass.

The composition was designed for the décor for a ball given in Paris by Count Etienne de Beaumont.

        Plate 56c

266 The Farmer's Wife

Tapestry: 82¾× 75⅝ in. (210× 192 cm.)
Lent by the artist

Tapestry woven from a *pastel* (1932) of the same dimensions, by the workshop of Marie Cuttoli.

        Plate 56b

267 Two Women

Tapestry: 77× 67¾ in. (196× 172 cm.)
Original design z.VIII.268
Lent by the artist

Tapestry woven from a *collage* (1934) of the same dimensions, by the workshop of Marie Cuttoli.

Paris, 1937/8   *Plate 56d*

268 Women at their Toilette

Oil and *papier collé* on canvas: 118⅛× 177½ in. (300× 450 cm.)
z.IX.103
Lent by the artist

This large *collage* composition was conceived as a cartoon for a tapestry which was never carried out.

Lenders

Addenda

Paris, 1909

269 Vase, Gourd and Fruit on a Table

Oil on canvas: $28\frac{3}{4} \times 23\frac{5}{8}$ in. (73×60 cm.)
Unsigned
z.II*126
Lent from a private collection, Paris
This still life should be compared with *The Fruit Dish* (cat. no.46) painted at the same time.

1915

270 Glass and Napkin

Oil on canvas: $13\frac{1}{2} \times 10\frac{5}{8}$ in. ($34\cdot3 \times 27$ cm.)
Signed bottom right: *Picasso*
Lent by Sir Herbert Read

Plates

Plate 1a   Self Portrait, 1901
32×22½ in.   *The artist* (13)

Plate 1b   Le Moulin de la Galette,
1900, 35×45¾ in.
Mr and Mrs J. K. Thannhauser (4)

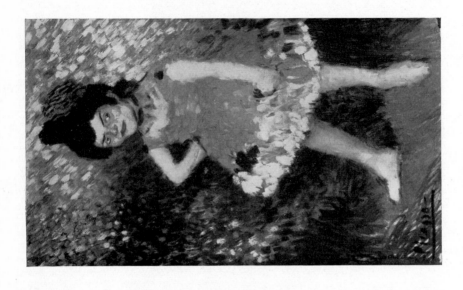

Plate 2b Dwarf Dancer, 1901, 40⅛ × 23⅝ in.
Museum of Modern Art, Barcelona (9)

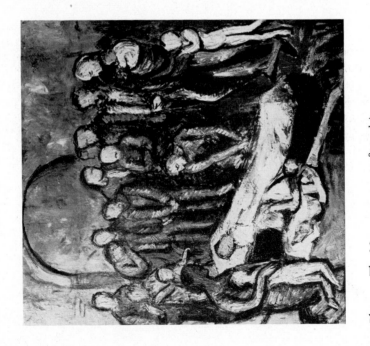

Plate 2a The Mourners, 1901, 39⅜ × 35½ in.
Mr Edward G. Robinson (8)

Plate 3b   Girl with a Fan, 1905, 39½ × 32 in.
The Hon. and Mrs W. Averell Harriman (26)

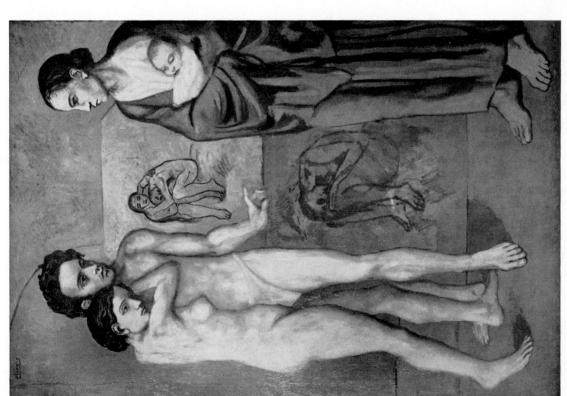

Plate 3a   La Vie, 1903, 77⅞ × 50⅞ in.   Cleveland Museum of Art (20)

a

b

c

d

e

f

g

h

i

j

Plate 4a Girl with Bare Feet, 1895, $29\frac{1}{4} \times 19\frac{1}{2}$in. *The artist* (1)

   b Interior of Tavern, 1897, $7 \times 9\frac{1}{2}$ in. *O'Hana Gallery* (2)

   c Portrait of the Artist's Sister, 1899, $59 \times 39\frac{1}{2}$ in. *The artist* (3)

   d Bullfight, 1901, $19\frac{1}{2} \times 25\frac{1}{2}$ in. *Mr Stavros S. Niarchos* (6)

   e Head of a Woman, 1900, 14×13 in. *The Hon. Michael Astor* (5)

   f On the Upper Deck, 1901, $19\frac{3}{8} \times 25\frac{1}{4}$ in. *Art Institute of Chicago* (10)

   g Child holding a Dove, 1901, $28\frac{3}{4} \times 21\frac{1}{4}$ in.
     The Dowager Lady Aberconway (14)

   h Blue Roofs, 1901, $15\frac{3}{4} \times 23\frac{5}{8}$ in. *Ashmolean Museum* (11)

   i Portrait of Gustave Coquiot, 1901, $39\frac{3}{8} \times 31\frac{7}{8}$ in.
     Musée National d'Art Moderne, Paris (12)

   j Auteuil Races, 1901, 18×28 in. *Mr Lee Hardy* (7)

Plate 5a Mother and Child, 1901, $35\frac{3}{4} \times 23\frac{5}{8}$ in. *Mr and Mrs William Goetz* (15)
   b Two Women at a Bar, 1902, $31\frac{1}{2} \times 36$ in.
      Mr Walter P. Chrysler, Jr. (16)
   c Girl with a Basket of Flowers, 1905, $59\frac{7}{8} \times 25\frac{3}{4}$ in. *Private Collection* (23)
   d Portrait of a Woman, 1904, $40 \times 29\frac{3}{4}$ in. *Matthiesen Gallery* (21)
   e Street in Barcelona, 1903, $23\frac{5}{8} \times 15\frac{3}{4}$ in. *The Hon. Michael Astor* (17)
   f Boy with Pipe, 1905, $39\frac{3}{8} \times 32$ in.
      The Hon. and Mrs John Hay Whitney (24)
   g Woman in a Chemise, c.1905, $28\frac{5}{8} \times 23\frac{5}{8}$ in. *The Tate Gallery* (22)
   h Dutch Girl, 1905, $30\frac{3}{4} \times 26\frac{1}{2}$ in. *Queensland Art Gallery, Brisbane* (25)
   i Girl with Pitcher, 1905, $39\frac{3}{8} \times 32$ in. *Mr Edward James* (27)
   j Boy and Horse, 1905, $19\frac{5}{8} \times 12\frac{5}{8}$ in. *The Tate Gallery* (28)

Plate 6a   The Soler Family, 1903
59 × 78¾ in.
Musée des Beaux-Arts, Liège (19)

Plate 6b   The Blind Man's Meal, 1903
37½ × 37¼ in.
Metropolitan Museum, New York (18)

Plate 7a   La Toilette, 1906, $59\frac{1}{2} \times 39\frac{1}{2}$ in.
Albright Art Gallery, Buffalo (29)

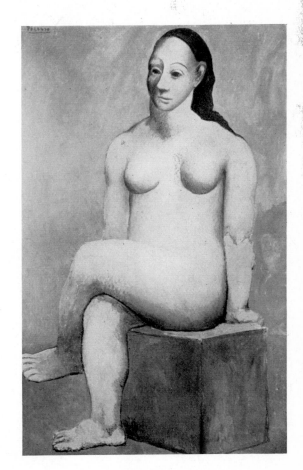

Plate 7b   Seated Female Nude, 1906, $59\frac{1}{2} \times 39\frac{3}{8}$ in.
National Gallery, Prague (32)

Plate 8a   Nude with a Towel, 1907, $45\frac{5}{8} \times 35\frac{1}{2}$ in.
La Vicomtesse de Noailles (39)

Plate 8b   Harvesters, 1907, $25\frac{5}{8} \times 31\frac{7}{8}$ in.   *Private Collection* (33)

Plate 9b Flowers, 1907, 36½ × 28½ in.
Mr and Mrs Ralph F. Colin (38)

Plate 9a Dancer, 1907, 59 × 39½ in.
Mr Walter P. Chrysler, Jr. (36)

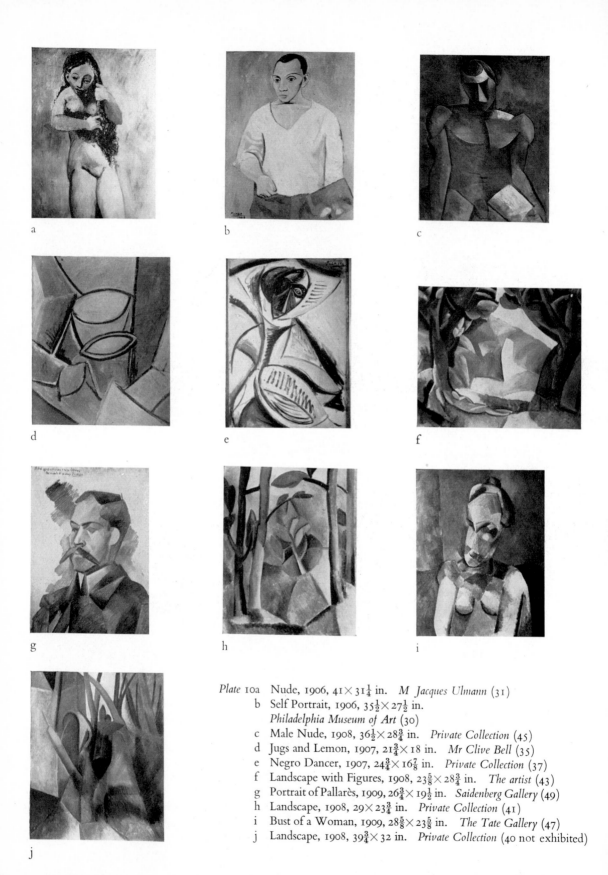

Plate 10a   Nude, 1906, 41×31¼ in.   *M Jacques Ulmann* (31)
      b   Self Portrait, 1906, 35½×27½ in.
         Philadelphia Museum of Art (30)
      c   Male Nude, 1908, 36½×28¾ in.   *Private Collection* (45)
      d   Jugs and Lemon, 1907, 21¾×18 in.   *Mr Clive Bell* (35)
      e   Negro Dancer, 1907, 24¾×16⅞ in.   *Private Collection* (37)
      f   Landscape with Figures, 1908, 23⅝×28¾ in.   *The artist* (43)
      g   Portrait of Pallarès, 1909, 26¾×19½ in.   *Saidenberg Gallery* (49)
      h   Landscape, 1908, 29×23¾ in.   *Private Collection* (41)
      i   Bust of a Woman, 1909, 28⅝×23⅝ in.   *The Tate Gallery* (47)
      j   Landscape, 1908, 39¾×32 in.   *Private Collection* (40 not exhibited)

a   b   c

d   e   f

g   h   i

Plate 11a   Nude, 1910, $73\frac{1}{4} \times 23\frac{5}{8}$ in.   *Private Collection* (54)
         b   Nude, 1910, $36\frac{1}{4} \times 28\frac{3}{4}$ in.   *The Tate Gallery* (53)
         c   Head of a Woman, 1910, $25\frac{1}{4} \times 20\frac{1}{4}$ in.   *Private Collection* (50)
         d   Glass and Straws, *c*.1911, $12 \times 10\frac{1}{4}$ in.   *Private Collection* (56)
         e   Still Life with Books and a Bottle, 1910/11, $15 \times 18\frac{1}{4}$ in.
             Miss J. E. Norton (55)
         f   The Mandolin Player, 1911, $39\frac{3}{8} \times 27\frac{1}{2}$ in.
             M Fernand Graindorge (57)
         g   Table, Glasses, Cups, Mandolin, 1911, $24\frac{1}{2} \times 19\frac{1}{2}$ in. *Lady Hulton* (59)
         h   Soldier and Girl, 1911, $45\frac{3}{4} \times 32$ in.   *Private Collection* (58)
         i   Still Life with Chair Caning, 1911/12, $10\frac{5}{8} \times 13\frac{3}{4}$ in. *The artist* (61)

Plate 12b Bather, 1908, 51¼ × 38¼ in. *Private Collection* (44)

Plate 12a Fruit Dish, 1908/9, 29¼ × 24 in.
Museum of Modern Art, New York (46)

Plate 13b   Landscape with Bridge, 1908, $31\frac{7}{8} \times 39\frac{3}{8}$ in.   *National Gallery, Prague* (42)

Plate 13a   The Reservoir, 1909, $23\frac{5}{8} \times 19\frac{3}{4}$ in.   *Private Collection* (48)

Plate 14b Portrait of Uhde, 1910, 30¾ × 22¾ in.
Private Collection (51)

Plate 14a Girl with a Mandolin, 1910, 39½ × 29 in.
Private Collection (52)

Plate 15b   The 'Aficionado', 1912, 53¼ × 32½ in.
Kunstmuseum, Basel (64)

Plate 15a   Man with a Pipe, 1911, 36⅞ × 23⅜ in.   *Private Collection* (60)

Plate 16a   Spanish Still Life, 1912, $18\frac{1}{8} \times 13$ in.   *Private Collection* (63)
    b   Bottle, Glass, Violin, 1912/13, $18\frac{1}{2} \times 24\frac{3}{4}$ in. *M Tristan Tzara* (65)
    c   Head, 1913?, $17\frac{1}{8} \times 13\frac{1}{8}$ in.   *Private Collection* (68)
    d   Head of a Girl, 1912/13, $23\frac{3}{4} \times 18\frac{1}{2}$ in.   *M Tristan Tzara* (66)
    e   Head of a Man, 1913, $24\frac{1}{4} \times 18\frac{1}{4}$ in.   *Mr Richard S. Zeisler* (69)
    f   Harlequin, 1913, $34\frac{3}{4} \times 18\frac{1}{4}$ in. *Municipal Museum, The Hague* (71)
    g   Violon au Cafe, 1913, $31\frac{7}{8} \times 21\frac{1}{4}$ in.   *M Siegfried Rosengart* (70)
    h   Student with Pipe, 1913/14, $28\frac{3}{4} \times 23\frac{1}{4}$ in. *Private Collection* (73)
    i   Glass and Dice, 1914, $9\frac{1}{2} \times 6\frac{1}{4}$ in.   *M Heinz Berggruen* (76)
    j   Guitar, Skull and Newspaper, 1914, $17\frac{1}{8} \times 24$ in.   *Private Collection* (74)

a

b

c

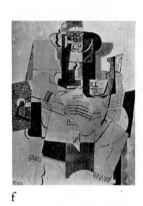

d

e

f

g

h

i

j

Plate 17a   Playing Card, Fruit Dish, Glass, 1914, 24× 18¾ in.   *Private Collection* (77)

    b   Guitar, Playing Card, Glass, Bottle of Bass, 1914, 18⅛× 21⅝ in.
        M César de Hauke (79)

    c   Still Life, 1914, 10× 18⅞ in.   *Private Collection* (75)

    d   Head of a Young Man, 1915, 10× 7¼ in.   *Mrs Louise R. Smith* (83)

    e   Still Life in a Landscape, 1915, 24½× 29½ in.   *M Heinz Berggruen* (82)

    f   Fruit Dish, Guitar, Bottle, 1914, 36¼× 29 in.   *Private Collection* (78)

    g   Harlequin with a Guitar, 1918, 13¾× 10⅝ in.   *M Heinz Berggruen* (88)

    h   Table in Front of a Window, 1919, 12¼× 8¾ in.
        M Siegfried Rosengart (90)

    i   Harlequin, 1917, 46⅛× 35 in.   *Museum of Modern Art, Barcelona* (86)

    j   Landscape, 1920, 20½× 27½ in.   *The artist* (93)

Plate 18a   Still Life with Gas Jet, 1912–13
27×21 in.   *Private Collection* (67)

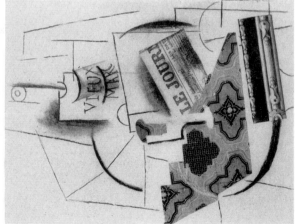

Plate 18b   Bottle of 'Vieux Marc', Glass

*Plate 19b Woman in an Armchair, 1913, 58¼ × 39 in.
Dr. I. Pudelko Eichmann (72)*

Plate 19a Man leaning on a Table, 1915, 78 × 52 in. Private Collection (81)

Plate 20b L'Italienne, 1917, 58⅝ × 39¾ in.
E. G. Bührle Collection (85)

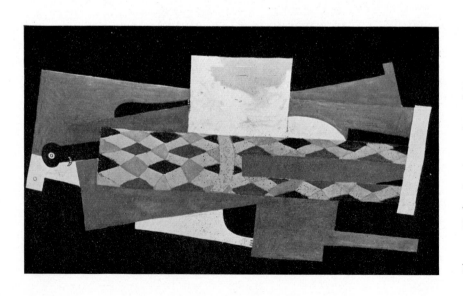

Plate 20a Harlequin, 1915, 72¼ × 41⅜ in.
Museum of Modern Art, New York (84)

Plate 21a Window Opening on to the Rue de Penthièvre,
1920, 64½ × 43 in.
Private Collection (92)

Plate 21b Harlequin, 1918, 57¾ × 26⅛ in.   *Mr and Mrs Joseph Pulitzer, Jr.* (87)

Plate 22b   Still Life on a Chest of Drawers, 1919, $31\frac{7}{8} \times 39\frac{3}{8}$ in.   *The artist* (91)

Plate 22a   Guitar, 1918, $31\frac{7}{8} \times 17\frac{3}{4}$ in.
Rijksmuseum Kröller-Müller, Otterlo (89)

Plate 23
Three Musicians, 1921
79 × 87¾ in.
Museum of Modern Art,
New York (97)

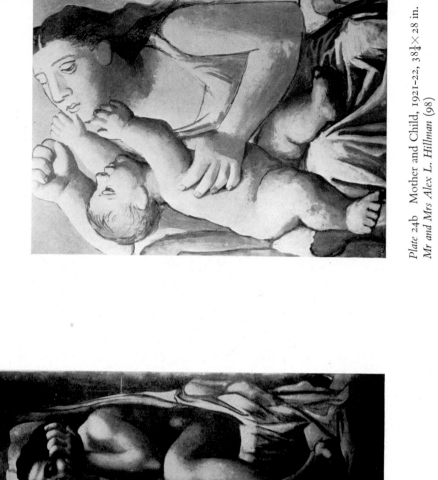

Plate 24b Mother and Child, 1921–22, 38¼×28 in.
Mr and Mrs Alex L. Hillman (98)

Plate 24a Two Seated Women, 1920, 76¾×64¼ in.
Mr Walter P. Chrysler, Jr. (94)

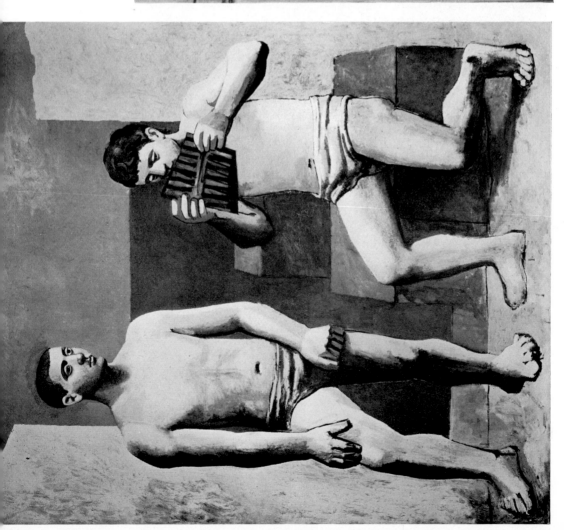

Plate 25b The Fish Net, 1925, $39\frac{3}{4} \times 32\frac{5}{8}$ in. *Private Collection* (111)

Plate 25a Pipes of Pan, 1923, $80\frac{1}{2} \times 68\frac{5}{8}$ in. *The artist* (104)

a

b

c

d

e

f

g

h

i

j

Plate 26a The Rape, 1920, $9\frac{3}{8} \times 12\frac{7}{8}$ in.   *Museum of Modern Art, New York* (95)

b Still Life with a Guitar, 1922, $32\frac{1}{2} \times 40\frac{1}{2}$ in.   *M Siegfried Rosengart* (101

c Nude Seated on a Rock, 1921, $5\frac{7}{8} \times 3\frac{7}{8}$ in.   *Mr James Thrall Soby* (96

d Fruit Dish, Bottle, Packet of Cigarettes, 1922, $14\frac{1}{4} \times 17\frac{3}{4}$ in.
   M Heinz Berggruen (102)

e Guitar on a Red Cloth, 1922, $32\frac{1}{8} \times 45\frac{7}{8}$ in.   *Private collection* (99)

f Woman and Child, 1922/23, $51\frac{1}{2} \times 38\frac{1}{4}$ in.
   Mr Walter P. Chrysler, Jr. (103)

g Seated Woman, 1923, $36\frac{1}{4} \times 28\frac{3}{4}$ in.   *The Tate Gallery* (105)

h The Race, 1922, $12\frac{7}{8} \times 16\frac{1}{4}$ in.   *The artist* (100)

i Woman Seated in a Red Chair, 1923, $39\frac{3}{8} \times 32$ in.
   Mr Edward James (106)

j Paul as Harlequin, 1924, $51\frac{1}{8} \times 38\frac{1}{8}$ in.   *The artist* (107)

a

b

c

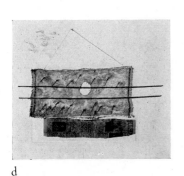

d

e

f

g

h

i

j

Plate 27a Landscape, 1914, 15×18⅛ in.   *M Heinz Berggruen* (108)

    b Girl with Mandolin, 1925, 51⅜×38⅝ in.   *Private Collection* (112)

    c Still Life with Apples, 1924, 14⅞×21½ in.
       Trustees of King's College, Cambridge (109)

    d Guitar, 1926, 38¼×51¼ in.   *The artist* (113)

    e Figure, 1927, 51×38⅛ in.   *The artist* (114)

    f Woman Sleeping in a Chair, 1927, 36¼×28¾ in.
       Betty Barman (115)

    g Woman in an Armchair, 1929, 76¾×51⅛ in.   *The artist* (119)

    h Bathers with a Ball, 1929, 6½×8¾ in.   *Private Collection* (118)

    i Standing Bather, 1929, 76¾×51¼ in.   *The artist* (120)

    j Head, 1929, 29×24 in.   *Private Collection* (122)

Plate 28a   Crucifixion, 1930, 20×26 in.
The artist (123)

Plate 28b   Three Dancers, 1925, 84⅝×56¼ in.
The artist (110)

Plate 29a   Seated Woman,, 1927, $51\frac{1}{8} \times 38\frac{1}{4}$ in.
Mr James Thrall Soby (116)

Plate 29b   Painter and Model, 1928, $51\frac{1}{2} \times 64$ in.
Mr Sidney Janis (117)

Plate 30a Pitcher and Bowl of Fruit, 1931, 51¼ × 64 in. *Private Collection* (125)

Plate 30b Women and Children
on the Beach, 1932, 31⅞ × 39⅜ in.
Mr Michael Hertz (130)

Plate 31a   Seated Bather, 1930, 64¼ × 51 in.
Museum of Modern Art, New York (124)

Plate 31b   Reclining Nude, 1936
51¼ × 63¾ in.   *Private Collection* (140)

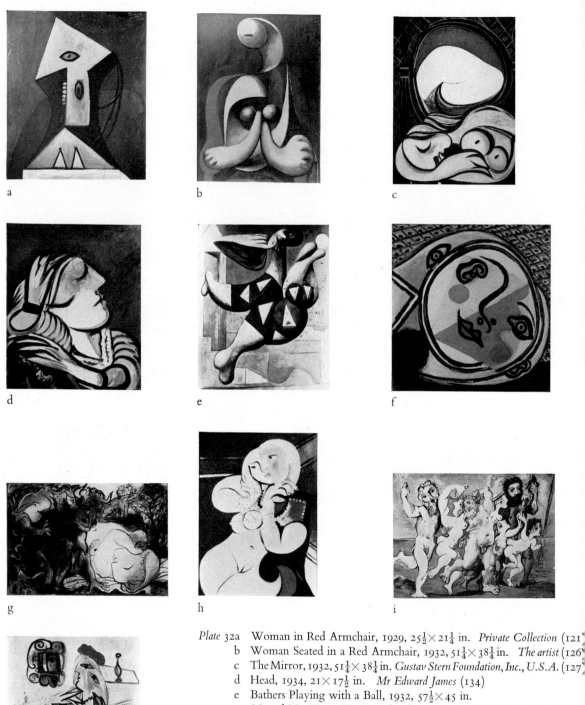

Plate 33a   Woman with a Hat, 1935, $23\frac{5}{8} \times 19\frac{3}{4}$ in. *M Georges Salles* (139)

    b   Still Life, 1936, $14\frac{1}{2} \times 23\frac{1}{2}$ in.   *Mrs A. T. Kessler* (141)

    c   Seated Woman with a Book, 1937, $51\frac{1}{8} \times 38\frac{1}{8}$ in.   *The artist* (142)

    d   Portrait of D.M., 1937, $36\frac{1}{4} \times 25\frac{1}{2}$ in.   *The artist* (148)

    e   Woman with a Cat, 1937, $31\frac{7}{8} \times 25\frac{1}{2}$ in. *Dr Henri Laugier* (147)

    f   Woman Weeping, 1937, $24\frac{3}{8} \times 20$ in.   *Mme Dora Maar* (144)

    g   Maïa with a Sailor Doll, 1938, $28\frac{3}{4} \times 23\frac{5}{8}$ in.   *The artist* (151)

    h   Cock, 1938, $30\frac{1}{2} \times 21\frac{1}{4}$ in.   *Mr and Mrs Ralph F. Colin* (152)

    i   Portrait of Nusch, 1937, $36\frac{1}{4} \times 25\frac{5}{8}$ in.   *The artist* (149)

    j   Portrait of Nusch, 1937, $21\frac{5}{8} \times 18\frac{1}{8}$ in. *M Heinz Berggruen* (150)

Plate 34a Horse's Head, 1937
$25\frac{1}{2} \times 36\frac{1}{4}$ in.   *The artist* (143)

Plate 34b   Bullfight, 1934, $38\frac{1}{4} \times 51\frac{1}{4}$ in.   *Mr and Mrs Victor W. Ganz* (137)

Plate 35a   Woman Weeping, 1937
$23\frac{1}{2} \times 19\frac{1}{4}$ in.   *Private Collection* (146)

te 35b   Woman and Dead Child, 1937, $51\frac{1}{4} \times 76\frac{3}{4}$ in. *The artist* (145)

Plate 36a   Still Life with Black Bull's Head, 1938, 38¼×51¼ in.
Colonel Valdemar Ebbesen (155)

Plate 36b   Two Women, 1935, 51×65 in.   *Musée National d'Art Moderne* (138)

Plate 37a   Cat Eating a Bird, 1939, 38× 50¾ in.   *Private Collection* (158)

Plate 37b   Soles, 1940, 23⅝× 36¼ in.   *Le Marquis de Pomereu* (161)

Plate 38b   Head of a Woman, 1943, $36\frac{1}{4} \times 28\frac{3}{4}$ in.
Private Collection (173)

Plate 38a   Woman Dressing her Hair, 1940, $51\frac{1}{4} \times 38\frac{1}{8}$ in
Mrs Louise R. Smith (162)

Plate 39b Still Life with Skull of a Bull, 1942, $57\frac{1}{8} \times 38\frac{1}{4}$ in.
M André Lefevre (167)

Plate 39a First Steps, 1943, $51\frac{1}{4} \times 38\frac{1}{4}$ in.
Yale University Art Gallery (170)

Plate 40a   Girl with an Artichoke, 1942
76¾× 52 in.
Mr Walter P. Chrysler, Jr. (168)

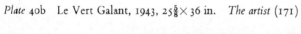

Plate 40b   Le Vert Galant, 1943, 25⅝× 36 in.   *The artist* (171)

a

b

c

d

e

f

g

h

i

Plate 42a Portrait of D.M., 1938, $28\frac{1}{2} \times 24\frac{1}{2}$ in. *Mr Walter P. Chrysler, Jr.* (153)

b Head of a Girl with Poem, 1938, $25\frac{5}{8} \times 19\frac{5}{8}$ in. *Private Collection* (154)

c The Yellow Sweater, 1939, $31\frac{7}{8} \times 25\frac{5}{8}$ in. *M Heinz Berggruen* (160)

d Still Life with Fish, 1936, $19\frac{3}{4} \times 24$ in. *McRoberts and Tunnard Gallery* (156)

e Portrait of D.M., 1941, $21\frac{5}{8} \times 18\frac{1}{8}$ in. *Estorick Collection* (164)

f Woman Lying on a Couch, 1939, $38\frac{1}{4} \times 51$ in. *Mr and Mrs Victor W. Ganz* (157)

g Cat Eating a Bird, 1939, $32 \times 39\frac{3}{8}$ in. *The artist* (159)

h Woman seated in a Chair, 1941/42, $51\frac{1}{4} \times 38\frac{1}{8}$ in. *M Heinz Berggruen* (166)

i Café at Royan, 1940, $38\frac{1}{4} \times 51\frac{1}{4}$ in. *The artist* (163)

a

b

c

d

e

f

g

h

Plate 43a Still Life with Sausage, 1941, $35 \times 25\frac{1}{2}$ in.
Mr and Mrs Victor W. Ganz (165)
b Reclining Nude, 1942, $51\frac{1}{4} \times 76\frac{3}{4}$ in. *Mr and Mrs Victor W. Ganz* (169)
c Woman and Rocking Chair, 1943, $63\frac{3}{4} \times 51\frac{1}{4}$ in.
Musée National d'Art Moderne (172)
d Woman in Green, 1943, 51×38 in.
Mr and Mrs James Johnson Sweeney (174)
e Still Life with Candle, 1944, $23\frac{5}{8} \times 36\frac{1}{4}$ in. *Mr Jacques Sarlie* (176)
f Head, 1944, $13\frac{7}{8} \times 8\frac{3}{4}$ in. *Private Collection* (177)
g Head of a Youth, 1943, $12\frac{3}{4} \times 10$ in. *Dr Henry M. Roland* (175)
h Cock and Knife, 1947, $31\frac{7}{8} \times 39\frac{3}{8}$ in. *Mr and Mrs Victor W. Ganz* (180)

Plate 44a   Portrait of a Painter
after El Greco, 1950, 40 × 32¼ in.
Mlle Angela Rosengart (184)

Plate 44b   The Kitchen, 1948, 68⅞ × 98⅜ in.
The artist (181)

Plate 45a   Skull of a Goat, Bottle and Candle, 1952, 35×45⅝ in.
The Tate Gallery (189)

Plate 45b   Women of Algiers, 1955, 44⅞× 57½ in.   *Mr and Mrs Victor W. Ganz* (196)

a   b   c

d   e   f

g   h   i

Plate 46a   Girl-Flower, 1946, $57\frac{1}{2} \times 35$ in.   *Mme Françoise Gilot* (179)
     b   Claude and Paloma, 1950, $51\frac{1}{4} \times 38\frac{1}{4}$ in.   *The artist* (183)
     c   Portrait of Françoise, 1949, 24×15 in.   *M Heinz Berggruen* (182)
     d   Chimneys of Vallauris, 1951, $23\frac{5}{8} \times 28\frac{3}{4}$ in.   *The artist* (185)
     e   Mother and Children with an Orange, 1951, $45\frac{1}{4} \times 34\frac{3}{4}$ in.
        The artist (186)
     f   The Knight (Sport of Pages), 1951, $21\frac{1}{4} \times 25\frac{1}{2}$ in.   *The artist* (187)
     g   Paloma Asleep, 1952, $44\frac{7}{8} \times 57\frac{1}{2}$ in.   *Mrs Louise R. Smith* (190)
     h   Moonlight at Vallauris, 1951, 54×41 in.   *Galerie de l'Europe* (188)
       Girl Reading with Red Background, 1953, $31\frac{7}{8} \times 39\frac{3}{8}$ in.
       Mrs Leon Bagrit (191)

a

b

c

d

e

f

g

h

i

j

Plate 47a Seated Nude, 1954, $51\frac{1}{4} \times 38\frac{1}{4}$ in. *M Siegfried Rosengart* (193)
   b Portrait of J.R. with Roses, 1954, $39\frac{3}{8} \times 31\frac{7}{8}$ in. *The artist* (194)
   c The Coiffure, 1954, $51\frac{5}{8} \times 38\frac{1}{4}$ in. *M Siegfried Rosengart* (192)
   d Seated Woman, 1955, $36\frac{1}{4} \times 28\frac{3}{4}$ in. *Mlle Angela Rosengart* (197)
   e Bullfight, 1956, $19\frac{5}{8} \times 24$ in. *Mr and Mrs Daniel Saidenberg* (201)
   f Still Life with Bull's Skull, 1958, $63\frac{3}{4} \times 51\frac{1}{4}$ in. *The artist* (261)
   g The Bay at Cannes, 1958, $51\frac{1}{4} \times 76\frac{3}{4}$ in. *The artist* (260)
   h L'Arlésienne, 1958, $24 \times 18\frac{1}{8}$ in. *The artist* (262)
   i The Studio at Cannes, 1956, $44\frac{1}{8} \times 57\frac{1}{2}$ in. *The artist* (200)
   j Composition with a Dalmatian Dog, 1959, 76×55 in.
      Galerie Louise Leiris (263)

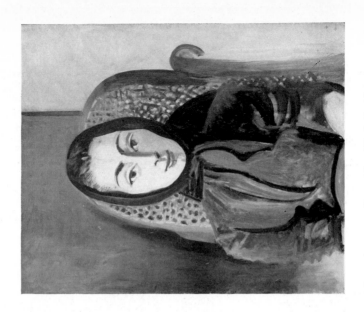

Plate 49b Jacqueline with a Black Scarf, 1954
36¼×28½ in.   *The artist* (195)

Plate 49a Las Meninas, 1957, 76½× 102 in.
The artist (202)

a

b

c

d

e

f

g

h

i

a

b

c

d

e

f

g

h

i

j

Plate 51a 28/8/57, Las Meninas, $7\frac{1}{8} \times 5\frac{1}{2}$ in. (212)
   b 4/9/57, Las Meninas, $13\frac{3}{4} \times 10\frac{5}{8}$ in. (213)
   c 4/9/57, Las Meninas, $13\frac{3}{4} \times 10\frac{5}{8}$ in. (214)
   d 4/9/57, Las Meninas, $18\frac{1}{8} \times 14\frac{3}{4}$ in. (215)
   e 5/9/57, Las Meninas, $13\frac{3}{4} \times 10\frac{5}{8}$ in. (216)
   f 6/9/57, Las Meninas, $16\frac{1}{8} \times 12\frac{3}{4}$ in. (217)
   g 6/9/57, Las Meninas, $18\frac{1}{8} \times 14\frac{3}{4}$ in. (218)
   h 6/9/57, The Pigeons, $39\frac{3}{8} \times 31\frac{1}{2}$ in. (219)
   i 6/9/57, The Pigeons, $39\frac{3}{8} \times 31\frac{1}{2}$ in. (220)
   j 7/9/57, The Pigeons, $13 \times 9\frac{3}{8}$ in. (221)

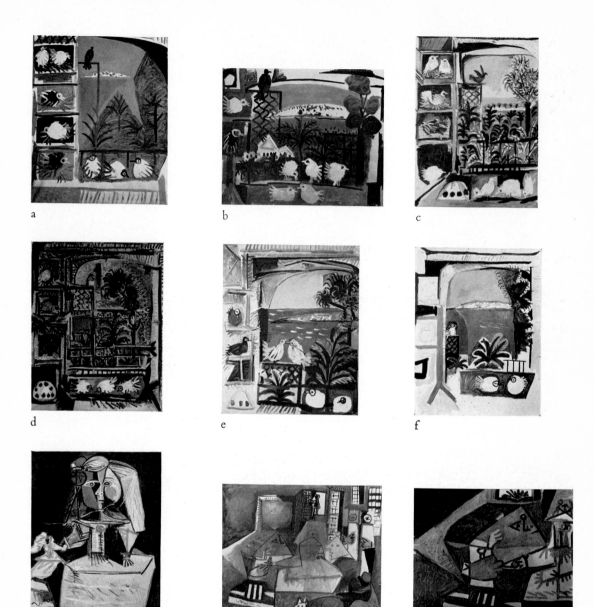

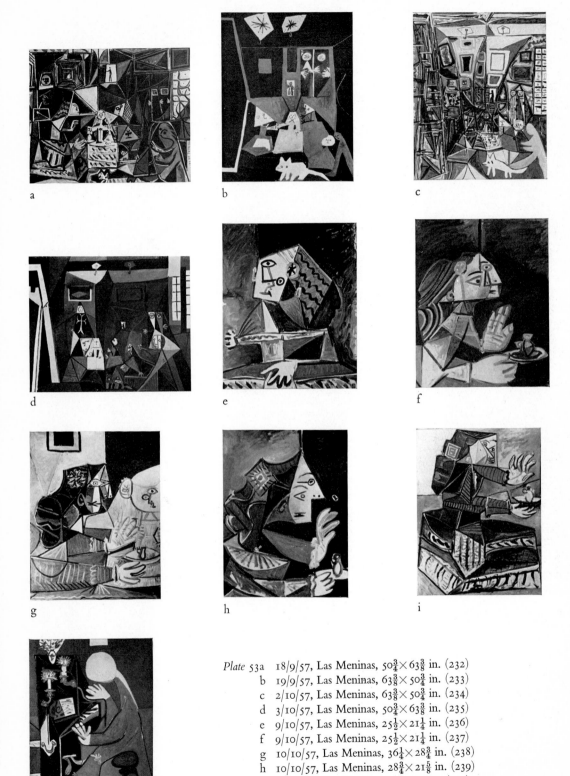

a

b

c

d

e

f

g

h

i

j

Plate 53a 18/9/57, Las Meninas, $50\frac{3}{4} \times 63\frac{3}{8}$ in. (232)
 b 19/9/57, Las Meninas, $63\frac{3}{8} \times 50\frac{3}{4}$ in. (233)
 c 2/10/57, Las Meninas, $63\frac{3}{8} \times 50\frac{3}{4}$ in. (234)
 d 3/10/57, Las Meninas, $50\frac{3}{4} \times 63\frac{3}{8}$ in. (235)
 e 9/10/57, Las Meninas, $25\frac{1}{2} \times 21\frac{1}{4}$ in. (236)
 f 9/10/57, Las Meninas, $25\frac{1}{2} \times 21\frac{1}{4}$ in. (237)
 g 10/10/57, Las Meninas, $36\frac{1}{4} \times 28\frac{3}{4}$ in. (238)
 h 10/10/57, Las Meninas, $28\frac{3}{4} \times 21\frac{5}{8}$ in. (239)
 i 10/10/57, Las Meninas, $45\frac{1}{4} \times 35$ in. (240)
 j 17/10/57, The Piano, $51\frac{1}{8} \times 37\frac{3}{4}$ in. (241)

Plate 54a 24/10/57, Las Meninas, 24×19¾ in. (242)

      b 24/10/57, Las Meninas, 51⅛×37¾ in. (243)

      c 24/10/57, Las Meninas, 51⅛×37¾ in. (244)

      d 24/10/57, Las Meninas, 51⅛×37¾ in. (245)

      e 8/11/57, Las Meninas, 51⅛×37¾ in. (246)

      f 15/11/57, Las Meninas, 51⅛×37¾ in. (247)

      g 15/11/57, Las Meninas, 51⅛×37¾ in. (248)

      h 17/11/57, Las Meninas, 13¾×10⅝ in. (249)

      i 17/11/57, Las Meninas, 9½×7½ in. (250)

a

b

c

d

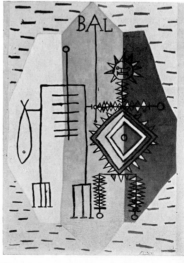

Plate 56a   Drop Curtain for 'Parade', 1917, 11×18 yds.
        Musée National d'Art Moderne, Paris (264)
    b   Two Women, 1934, 77×67¾ in.   *The artist* (267)
    c   The Farmer's Wife, 1932, 82¾×75⅝ in.
        The artist (266)
    d   Women at their Toilette, 1937/8, 118⅛×177½ in.
        The artist (268)
    e   Composition for a 'Mardi-Gras' Ball, 1923,
        155×84¼ in.   *The Chrysler Art Museum,
        Provincetown, Mass.* (265)

e